MEI STRUCTURED MATHEMATICS

THIRD EDITION

Mechanics 4

ONE WEEK LOAN

Pat Bryden
Cliff Pavelin

Series Editor: Roger

Acknowledgements

We are grateful to the following companies, institutions and individuals who have given permission to reproduce photographs in this book. Every effort has been made to trace and acknowledge ownership of copyright. The publishers will be glad to make suitable arrangements with any copyright holders whom it has not been possible to contact.

Photos   page 32 © China Photo/Reuters/CORBIS; page 59 © Royalty-Free/CORBIS; page 74 left © Hubert Stadler/CORBIS, middle © John and Lisa Merrill/CORBIS, right © Kim Sayer/CORBIS; page 106 © Vince Streano/CORBIS; page 116 © Duomo/CORBIS; page 144 left © Jennie Woodcock; Reflections Photolibrary/CORBIS, middle © Richard Cummins/CORBIS, right © BDI images.

OCR, AQA and Edexcel accept no responsibility whatsoever for the accuracy or method of working in the answers given.

Papers used in this book are natural, renewable, and recyclable products. They are made from wood grown in sustainable forests. The logging and manufacturing processes conform to the environmental regulations of the country of origin.

Orders: please contact Bookpoint Ltd, 78 Milton Park, Abingdon, Oxon OX14 4TD. Telephone: (44) 01235 827720, Fax: (44) 01235 400454. Lines are open from 9 am to 6 pm, Monday to Saturday, with a 24-hour message-answering service. You can also order from our website at *www.hoddereducation.co.uk.*

British Library Cataloguing in Publication Data
A catalogue record for this title is available from The British Library.

ISBN-10: 0 340 889985
ISBN-13: 9780 340 889985

First Edition Published 1996
This title was not published as part of the second edition of MEI Structured Mathematics.
Third Edition Published 2005
Impression number   10 9 8 7 6 5 4 3 2 1
Year   2010 2009 2008 2007 2006 2005

Copyright © 1996, 2004, Pat Bryden, Cliff Pavelin

Typeset by Phoenix Photosetting, Lordswood, Chatham, Kent.
Printed in Great Britain for Hodder Murray, a member of the Hodder Headline Group, 338 Euston Road, London NW1 3BH by Martins The Printers, Berwick-upon-Tweed.

MEI Structured Mathematics

Mathematics is not only a beautiful and exciting subject in its own right but also one that underpins many other branches of learning. It is consequently fundamental to the success of a modern economy.

MEI Structured Mathematics is designed to increase substantially the number of people taking the subject post-GCSE, by making it accessible, interesting and relevant to a wide range of students.

It is a credit accumulation scheme based on 45 hour units which may be taken individually or aggregated to give Advanced Subsidiary (AS) and Advanced GCSE (A Level) qualifications in Mathematics and Further Mathematics. The units may also be used to obtain credit towards other types of qualification.

The course is examined by OCR (previously the Oxford and Cambridge Schools Examination Board) with examinations held in January and June each year.

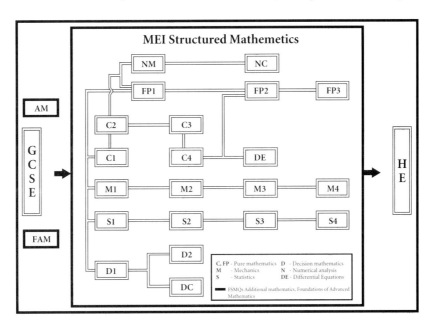

This is one of the series of books written to support the course. Its position within the whole scheme can be seen in the diagram above.

Mathematics in Education and Industry (MEI) is an independent curriculum development body which aims to promote links between education and industry in mathematics. MEI produce relevant examination specifications at GCSE, AS and A Level (including Further Mathematics) and for Free Standing Mathematics Qualifications (FSMQs); these are examined by OCR.

In partnership with Hodder Murray, MEI are responsible for three major series of textbooks: Formula One Maths for Key Stage 3, Hodder Mathematics for GCSE and the MEI Structured Mathematics series, including this book, for AS and A Level.

As well as textbooks, MEI take a leading role in the development of on-line resources to support mathematics. The books in this series are complemented by a major MEI website providing full solutions to the exercises, extra questions including on-line multiple choice tests, interactive demonstrations of the mathematics, schemes of work, and much more.

In recent years MEI have worked hard to promote Further Mathematics and, in conjunction with the DfES, they are now establishing the national network of Further Mathematics Centres.

MEI are committed to supporting the professional development of teachers. In addition to a programme of Continual Professional Development, MEI, in partnership with several universities, co-ordinate the Teaching Advanced Mathematics programme, a course designed to give teachers the skills and confidence to teach A Level mathematics successfully.

Much of the work of MEI is supported by the Gatsby Charitable Foundation.

MEI is a registered charity and a charitable company.

MEI's website and email addresses are *www.mei.org.uk* and *office@mei.org.uk*.

Introduction

This is the fourth in the series of books written to support the Mechanics components of MEI Structured Mathematics and covers the last of these components. As well as supporting the MEI scheme, *Mechanics 4* is suitable if you are studing Mechanics or Applied Mathematics as part of any A level Further Mathematics course or as part of a degree course.

Like the other books in the series, *Mechanics 4* presents the subject as a powerful and exciting means of modelling real situations, and contains several experiments and investigations for you to carry out. In the belief that an informed and intuitive understanding of mathematical results is necessary to practising applied mathematicians, engineers and scientists, we have taken every opportunity to apply techniques to interesting problems in the real world while at the same time encouraging you to develop an understanding of the mathematics involved.

Mechanics 4 builds on the basic mechanical principles introduced in the earlier books and develops and exploits the use of calculus. These are applied to a range of topics including the motion of bodies under variable forces, rotation of rigid bodies, variable mass and the application of energy methods to stability problems.

We would like to thank the many people who have given help and advice with this book as it has developed, including David Edsall, Robin Grayson, Val Hanrahan, David Holland, Mike Jones, Alan Bryden, Penny Nicholson and our series editor Roger Porkess. Acknowledgements are also due to the examination boards who have allowed us to use their questions in the exercises.

Readers who are interested in a possible career in mathematics may wish to visit www.mathscareers.org.uk.

Pat Bryden and Cliff Pavelin

Key to symbols in this book

?   This symbol means that you may want to discuss a point with your teacher. If you are working on your own there are answers in the back of the book. It is important, however, that you have a go at answering the questions before looking up the answers if you are to understand the mathematics fully.

⚠   This is a warning sign. It is used where a common mistake, misunderstanding or tricky point is being described.

▯   This is the ICT icon. It indicates where you should use a graphic calculator or a computer.

e   This symbol and a dotted line down the right-hand side of the page indicates material which is beyond the criteria for the unit but which is included for completeness.

☆☆   Harder questions are indicated with stars. Many of these go beyond the usual examination standard.

Contents

Variable forces

Is it possible to fire a projectile up to the moon?

The Earth to the Moon *by Jules Verne (1865)*

In his book, Jules Verne says that this is possible ... 'provided it possesses an initial velocity of 12 000 yards per second. In proportion as we recede from the Earth the action of gravitation diminishes in the inverse ratio of the square of the distance; that is to say at three times a given distance the action is nine times less. Consequently the weight of a shot will decrease and will become reduced to zero at the instant that the attraction of the moon exactly counterpoises that of the Earth; at $\frac{47}{52}$ of its journey. There the projectile will have no weight whatever; and if it passes that point it will fall into the moon by the sole effect of lunar attraction.'

❓ If an *unpowered* projectile could be launched from the Earth with a high enough speed in the right direction, it would reach the moon.

What forces act on the projectile during its journey?

How near to the moon will it get if its initial speed is not *quite* enough?

In Jules Verne's story, three men and two dogs were sent to the moon inside a projectile fired from an enormous gun. Although this is completely impracticable, the basic mathematical ideas in the passage above are correct. As a projectile moves further from the Earth and nearer to the moon, the gravitational attraction of the Earth decreases and that of the moon increases. In many of the dynamics problems you have met so far it has been assumed that forces are *constant*, whereas on Jules Verne's space missile the total force *varies* continuously as the motion proceeds.

You have already met problems involving variable force. When an object is suspended on a spring and bounces up and down, the varying tension in the spring leads to *simple harmonic motion*. You will also be aware that air resistance depends on velocity.

Gravitation, spring tension and air resistance all give rise to variable force problems, the subject of this chapter.

Newton's second law as a differential equation

Calculus techniques are used extensively in mechanics and you will already have used differentiation and integration in earlier work. In this book you will see how essential calculus methods are in the solution of a variety of problems.

To solve variable force problems, you can use Newton's second law to give an equation for the *instantaneous* value of the acceleration. When the mass of a body is constant, this can be written in the form of a *differential equation*.

$$F = m\frac{dv}{dt}$$

It can also be written as

$$F = mv\frac{dv}{ds}.$$

This follows from the chain rule for differentiation.

$$\frac{dv}{dt} = \frac{dv}{ds} \times \frac{ds}{dt}$$

$$= v\frac{dv}{ds}$$

Note

Here and throughout this chapter the mass, *m*, is assumed to be constant. Jules Verne's spacecraft was a projectile fired from a gun. It was not a *rocket* whose mass varies, due to ejection of fuel. Rocket motion is considered in Chapter 2.

Deriving the constant acceleration formulae

To see the difference in use between the $\frac{dv}{dt}$ and $v\frac{dv}{ds}$ forms of acceleration, it is worth looking at the case where the force, and therefore the acceleration, $\frac{F}{m}$ is *constant* (say *a*). Starting from the $\frac{dv}{dt}$ form

$$\frac{dv}{dt} = a$$

Integrating gives

$$v = u + at$$

where *u* is the constant of integration ($v = u$ when $t = 0$).

Since $v = \frac{ds}{dt}$, integrating again gives

$$s = ut + \tfrac{1}{2}at^2 + s_0$$

assuming the displacement is s_0 when $t = 0$.

These are the familiar formulae for motion under constant acceleration.

Starting from the $v\dfrac{\mathrm{d}v}{\mathrm{d}s}$ form

$$v\frac{\mathrm{d}v}{\mathrm{d}s}=a$$

Separating the variables and integrating gives

$$\int v\,\mathrm{d}v=\int a\,\mathrm{d}s$$

$$\Rightarrow\qquad \tfrac{1}{2}v^2=as+k$$

where k is the constant of integration.

Assuming $v=u$ when $s=0$, $k=\tfrac{1}{2}u^2$, so the formula becomes

$$v^2=u^2+2as$$

This is another of the standard constant acceleration formulae. Notice that *time is not involved* when you start from the $v\dfrac{\mathrm{d}v}{\mathrm{d}s}$ form of acceleration.

Deriving equations for simple harmonic motion

Another case where the $v\dfrac{\mathrm{d}v}{\mathrm{d}s}$ form of the acceleration is useful is in finding solutions to the simple harmonic motion equation. This example also illustrates how trigonometrical substitutions are used to perform some integrations.

When the force on a body is proportional to its displacement from a fixed point, O, and is directed towards O, Newton's second law gives an equation of this form.

$$\frac{\mathrm{d}^2x}{\mathrm{d}t^2}=-\omega^2x$$

Writing the acceleration as $v\dfrac{\mathrm{d}v}{\mathrm{d}x}$ gives

$$v\frac{\mathrm{d}v}{\mathrm{d}x}=-\omega^2x.$$

Separating variables gives

$$\int v\,\mathrm{d}v=-\int \omega^2x\,\mathrm{d}x$$

$$\Rightarrow\qquad \tfrac{1}{2}v^2=-\tfrac{1}{2}\omega^2x^2+c.$$

Using $x=a$ when $v=0$ gives $c=\tfrac{1}{2}\omega^2a^2$ and rearranging gives the familiar

$$v^2=\omega^2\left(a^2-x^2\right).$$

To find x in terms of t write

$$v = \omega\sqrt{a^2 - x^2}$$

or
$$\frac{dx}{dt} = \omega\sqrt{a^2 - x^2},$$

Then $\displaystyle\int \frac{dx}{\sqrt{a^2 - x^2}} = \int \omega\, dt = \omega t + \varepsilon$ ①

where ε is the constant of integration.

The first integral can be found by substituting $x = a \sin u$ so that

$$\frac{dx}{du} = a\cos u \quad \text{and} \quad dx = a\cos u\, du.$$

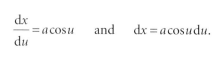

Notice that x is written as a function of u rather than u as a function of x. This means that you have to differentiate with respect to u.

Substituting for x and dx in the integral in terms of u gives

$$\int \frac{dx}{\sqrt{a^2 - x^2}} = \int \frac{a\cos u\, du}{\sqrt{a^2 - a^2\sin^2 u}}.$$

$\sqrt{a^2 - a^2\sin^2 u} = a\cos u$ so the integral becomes $\displaystyle\int du = u = \arcsin\frac{x}{a}.$

Hence $\arcsin\dfrac{x}{a} = \omega t + \varepsilon$ (from ①)

giving $x = a\sin(\omega t + \varepsilon)$.

This equation can be written in the different forms

$$x = a\cos(\omega t + \varepsilon')$$

and $\quad x = A\sin\omega t + B\cos\omega t$

if required (see *Mechanics 3*).

ACTIVITY 1.1   Use the substitution $x = a\cos u$ to find an expression for $\displaystyle\int \frac{-dx}{\sqrt{a^2 - x^2}}$.

Solving *F = ma* for variable force

When the force is continuously *variable*, you write Newton's second law in the form of a differential equation and then solve it using one of the forms of acceleration $v\dfrac{dv}{ds}$ or $\dfrac{dv}{dt}$. The choice depends on the particular problem. Some guidelines are given below and you should check these with the examples which follow.

Normally, the resulting differential equation can be solved by separating the variables.

The force is a function of time

When the force is a function, $F(t)$, of time you use $a = \dfrac{dv}{dt}$.

$$F(t) = m\frac{dv}{dt}$$

Separating the variables and integrating gives

$$m\int dv = \int F(t)dt.$$

Assuming you can solve the integral on the right-hand side, you then have v in terms of t.

Writing v as $\dfrac{ds}{dt}$, the displacement as a function of time can be found by integrating again.

The force is a function of displacement

When the force is a function, $F(s)$, of displacement, you normally start from

$$F(s) = mv\frac{dv}{ds}$$

then $\quad \int F(s)ds = m\int v\,dv.$

The force is a function of velocity

When the force is given as a function, $F(v)$, of velocity, you have a choice. You can use

$$F(v) = m\frac{dv}{dt}$$

or $\quad F(v) = mv\dfrac{dv}{ds}.$

You can separate the variables in both forms; use the first if you are interested in behaviour over time and the second when you wish to involve displacement.

ⓔ Using the second derivative

When F is a *linear function* of velocity or displacement, or both, another possible starting point is to use the second derivative, $\dfrac{d^2s}{dt^2}$.

$$F = m\frac{d^2s}{dt^2}$$

This gives a second-order linear differential equation which can be solved by the methods described in *Differential Equations*. The displacement is then given in terms of time without finding the velocity first. You can use the same method for the simple harmonic motion equation. There is a reminder in Appendix 2.

Variable force examples

The three examples that follow show the approaches used when the force is given respectively as a function of time, displacement and velocity.

When you are solving these problems, it is important to be clear about which direction is positive *before* writing down an equation of motion.

EXAMPLE 1.1

A crate of mass m is freely suspended at rest from a crane. When the operator begins to lift the crate further, the tension in the suspending cable increases uniformly from mg newtons to $1.2\,mg$ newtons over a period of 2 seconds.

(i) What is the tension in the cable t seconds after the lifting has begun ($t \leqslant 2$)?
(ii) What is the velocity after 2 seconds?
(iii) How far has the crate risen after 2 seconds?

Assume the situation may be modelled with air resistance and cable stretching ignored. Take g as 10 ms^{-2}.

SOLUTION

When the crate is at rest it is in equilibrium and so the tension, T, in the cable equals the weight mg of the crate. After time $t = 0$, the tension increases, so there is a net upward force and the crate rises, see figure 1.1.

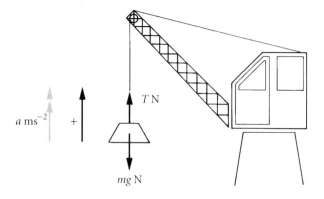

Figure 1.1

(i) The tension increases uniformly by $0.2mg$ newtons in 2 seconds, i.e. it increases by $0.1mg$ newtons per second, see figure 1.2. After t seconds, the tension is

$$T = mg + 0.1mgt.$$

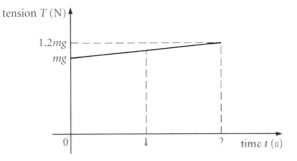

Figure 1.2

(ii) As the force is a function of time use $a = \dfrac{\mathrm{d}v}{\mathrm{d}t}$. Then at any moment in the 2-second period, $F = ma$ gives

$$\left(mg + 0.1mgt\right) - mg = m\dfrac{\mathrm{d}v}{\mathrm{d}t}$$

upwards is positive

$$\Rightarrow \qquad \dfrac{\mathrm{d}v}{\mathrm{d}t} = 0.1gt$$

Integrating gives

$$v = 0.05gt^2 + k$$

where k is the constant of integration.

When $t = 0$, the crate has not quite begun to move, so $v = 0$. This gives $k = 0$ and $v = 0.05gt^2$.

When t is 2,

$$v = 0.05 \times 10 \times 4$$
$$= 2.$$

The velocity after 2 seconds is 2 ms^{-1}.

(iii) To find the displacement s, write v as $\dfrac{\mathrm{d}s}{\mathrm{d}t}$ and integrate again.

$$\dfrac{\mathrm{d}s}{\mathrm{d}t} = 0.05gt^2$$

$$s = \int 0.05gt^2 \, \mathrm{d}t$$

$$s = 0.05g \times \tfrac{1}{3}t^3 + c$$

When $t = 0$, $s = 0 \Rightarrow c = 0$.

When $t = 2$ and $g = 10$, $s = \tfrac{4}{3}$.

The crate moves $\tfrac{4}{3}$ m in 2 seconds.

The displacement cannot be obtained by the formula $s = \frac{1}{2}(u+v)t$, which would give the answer 2 m. Why not?

EXAMPLE 1.2

A prototype of Jules Verne's projectile, mass m, is launched vertically upwards from the Earth's surface but only just reaches a height of one tenth of the Earth's radius before falling back. When the height, s, above the surface is small compared with the radius of the Earth, R, the magnitude of the earth's gravitational force on the projectile may be modelled as $mg\left(1 - \frac{2s}{R}\right)$, where g is gravitational acceleration at the Earth's surface.

Assuming all other forces can be neglected
(i) write down a differential equation of motion involving s and velocity, v
(ii) integrate this equation and hence obtain an expression for the loss of kinetic energy of the projectile between its launch and rising to a height s
(iii) show that the launch velocity is $0.3\sqrt{2gR}$.

SOLUTION

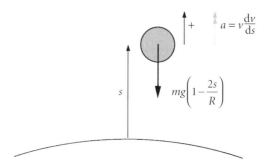

Figure 1.3

(i) Taking the upward direction as positive, the force on the projectile is $-mg\left(1 - \frac{2s}{R}\right)$. The force is a function of s, so start from the equation of motion in the form

$$mv\frac{dv}{ds} = -mg\left(1 - \frac{2s}{R}\right)$$

(ii) Separating the variables and integrating gives

$$\int mv\,dv = -\int mg\left(1 - \frac{2s}{R}\right)ds$$

$$\Rightarrow \qquad \tfrac{1}{2}mv^2 = -mgs + \frac{mgs^2}{R} + k.$$

> You would normally divide the equation by m, but it is useful to leave it in here in order to get kinetic energy directly from $\int mv\,dv$.

Writing v_0 for the launch velocity, $v = v_0$ when $s = 0$, so $k = \frac{1}{2}mv_0^2$ and rearranging gives

$$\tfrac{1}{2}mv_0^2 - \tfrac{1}{2}mv^2 = mgs - \frac{mgs^2}{R}. \qquad \text{①}$$

The left-hand side is the loss of kinetic energy, so

$$\text{loss of KE} = mgs - \frac{mgs^2}{R}.$$

> You can check that this is dimensionally consistent to give you confidence that your working is correct.

(iii) Dividing equation ① by m and multiplying by 2 gives

$$v_0^2 - v^2 = 2gs - \frac{2gs^2}{R}.$$

If the projectile just reaches a height $s = \dfrac{R}{10}$, then the velocity v is zero at that point.

Substituting $s = \dfrac{R}{10}$ and $v = 0$ gives

$$v_0^2 = 2g\left(\frac{R}{10}\right) - \frac{2gR^2}{100R}$$

$$= \frac{18gR}{100}$$

$$\Rightarrow \qquad v_0 = \frac{3}{10}\sqrt{2gR}$$

So the launch velocity is $0.3\sqrt{2gR}$.

EXAMPLE 1.3

A body of mass 2 kg, initially at rest on a smooth horizontal plane, is subjected to a horizontal force of magnitude $\dfrac{1}{2v+1}$ N, where v is the velocity of the body ($v > 0$).

(i) Find the time when the velocity is $1\,\text{ms}^{-1}$.

(ii) Find the displacement when the velocity is $1\,\text{ms}^{-1}$.

SOLUTION

(i) Using $F = ma = m\dfrac{\mathrm{d}v}{\mathrm{d}t}$

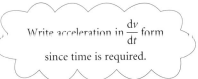

> Write acceleration in $\dfrac{\mathrm{d}v}{\mathrm{d}t}$ form since time is required.

$$\frac{1}{2v+1} = 2\frac{\mathrm{d}v}{\mathrm{d}t}.$$

Separating the variables gives

$$\int dt = \int 2(2v+1)\,dv$$

$$\Rightarrow \qquad t = 2v^2 + 2v + k.$$

When $t = 0$, $v = 0$ so $k = 0$ and therefore

$$t = 2v^2 + 2v$$

When $v = 1$, $t = 4$. That is, when the velocity is $1\ \text{ms}^{-1}$, the time is 4 seconds.

(ii) $F = ma = mv\dfrac{dv}{ds}$

> Write acceleration in $v\dfrac{dv}{ds}$ form since displacement is required.

$$\frac{1}{2v+1} = 2v\frac{dv}{ds}.$$

Separating the variables gives

$$\int ds = \int 2v(2v+1)\,dv$$

$$\Rightarrow \qquad s = \tfrac{4}{3}v^3 + v^2 + k.$$

When $s = 0$, $v = 0$ so $k = 0$ and therefore

$$s = \tfrac{4}{3}v^3 + v^2$$

When $v = 1$, $s = \tfrac{7}{3}$. When the velocity is $1\ \text{ms}^{-1}$, the displacement is $2\tfrac{1}{3}\ \text{m}$.

EXERCISE 1A

1 Use suitable substitutions (see page 4) to find the following integrals.

(i) $\displaystyle\int \frac{dv}{\sqrt{4-v^2}}$ (ii) $\displaystyle\int_0^{1.5} \frac{dx}{\sqrt{9-x^2}}$ (iii) $\displaystyle\int \frac{12\,dy}{\sqrt{9-4y^2}}$

2 (i) Use the substitution $x = 2\tan u$ to find $\displaystyle\int \frac{dx}{4+x^2}$.

(ii) Use a similar substitution to calculate $\displaystyle\int_0^{\frac{1}{2}} \frac{dx}{1+4x^2}$.

3 Each of the parts (i) to (viii) of this question assumes a body of mass 1 kg under the influence of a single force F N in a constant direction but with a variable magnitude given as a function of velocity, $v\ \text{ms}^{-1}$, displacement, s m, or time, t seconds.

In each case, express $F = ma$ as a differential equation using either

$a = \dfrac{dv}{dt}$ or $a = v\dfrac{dv}{ds}$ as appropriate. Then separate the variables and integrate

giving the result in the required form and leaving an arbitrary constant in the answer.

(i)	$F = 2v$	express s in terms of v
(ii)	$F = 2v$	express v in terms of t
(iii)	$F = 2\sin 3t$	express v in terms of t
(iv)	$F = -v^2$	express v in terms of t
(v)	$F = -v^2$	express v in terms of s
(vi)	$F = -4s + 2$	express v in terms of s
(vii)	$F = -2v - 3v^2$	express s in terms of v
(viii)	$F = 1 + v^2$	express s in terms of v

4 Each of the parts **(i)** to **(viii)** of this question assumes a body of mass 1 kg under the influence of a single force F N in a constant direction but with a variable magnitude given as a function of velocity, v ms^{-1}, displacement, s m, or time, t seconds. The body is initially at rest at a point O.

In each case, write down the equation of motion and solve it to supply the required information.

(i) $F = 2t^2$ find v when $t = 2$

(ii) $F = -\dfrac{1}{(s+1)^2}$ find v when $s = -\dfrac{1}{9}$

(iii) $F = \dfrac{1}{s+3}$ find v when $s = 3$

(iv) $F = \dfrac{1}{v+1}$ find t when $v = 3$

(v) $F = 1 + v^2$ find t when $v = 1$

(vi) $F = 5 - 3v$ find t when $v = 1$

(vii) $F = 1 - v^2$ find t when $v = 0.5$

(**Hint:** Use partial fractions.)

(viii) $F = 1 - v^2$ find s when $v = 0.5$

5 A horse pulls a 500 kg cart from rest until the speed, v, is about 5 ms^{-1}. Over this range of speeds, the magnitude of the force exerted by the horse can be modelled by $500(v + 2)^{-1}$ N. Neglecting resistance,

(i) write down an expression for $v\dfrac{dv}{ds}$ in terms of v

(ii) show by integration that when the velocity is 3 ms^{-1}, the cart has travelled 18 m

(iii) write down an expression for $\dfrac{dv}{dt}$ and integrate to show that the velocity is 3 ms^{-1} after 10.5 seconds

(iv) show that $v = -2 + \sqrt{4 + 2t}$

(v) integrate again to derive an expression for s in terms of t, and verify that after 10.5 seconds, the cart has travelled 18 m.

Gravitational force

Gravity is one of the fundamental forces of the universe, responsible for the motions of the planets, satellites and comets and indeed for the large-scale structure of the universe. All bodies attract each other by a gravitational force. It is very tiny for pairs of everyday objects, but large and important for objects of an astronomical size, such as the sun, the moon and the planets. Two particles attract each other with a force proportional to the product of their masses, m_1m_2, and inversely proportional to the square of the distance, r, between them.

$$\text{force} = \frac{Gm_1m_2}{r^2}$$

The constant G is known as the gravitational constant. For uniform spherical bodies, the force is along the line joining their centres and the distance is measured between their centres.

At the Earth's *surface*, an object of mass m is attracted to the centre by a force $\dfrac{GMm}{R^2}$, where M is the mass of the Earth and R is its radius.

Applying Newton's second law gives

$$\frac{GMm}{R^2} = ma.$$

So a, the acceleration of a body at the Earth's surface, is $\dfrac{GM}{R^2}$. This is g, the acceleration due to gravity. The Earth is so large that g can be assumed to be constant near to the surface. However, for objects such as meteorites or returning spacecraft, the continuous change in the gravitational force due to the changing distance from the centre of the Earth must be taken into account when the motion is analysed.

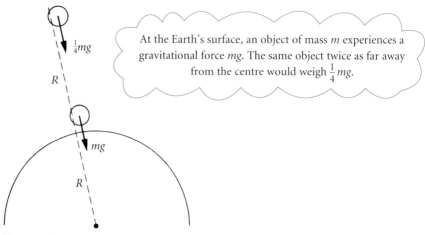

At the Earth's surface, an object of mass m experiences a gravitational force mg. The same object twice as far away from the centre would weigh $\frac{1}{4}mg$.

Figure 1.4

EXAMPLE 1.4

(i) Denoting the Earth's radius by R metres, show that the gravitational force on a body of mass m kg above the Earth's surface and a distance s metres from the Earth's centre ($s > R$) is $\dfrac{mgR^2}{s^2}$.

(ii) A projectile is fired vertically from the Earth's surface with an initial velocity of u ms^{-1} and reaches a maximum height of h m.
Derive from Newton's second law an expression giving u^2 in terms of R, g and h. (Neglect air resistance.)

(iii) For what launch speed would the projectile just reach a height equal to the radius of the Earth, 6400 km? (Use $g = 9.8$ ms^{-2}.)

(iv) What is the minimum launch speed if the projectile is never to return?

SOLUTION

(i) At the Earth's surface, the force on a body of mass m is $\dfrac{GMm}{R^2}$ newtons. So

$$\frac{GMm}{R^2} = \text{mass} \times \text{acceleration} = mg$$

$$\Rightarrow \qquad GM = gR^2$$

Above the Earth's surface at a distance s metres from the centre, the force on a body of mass m is

$$\frac{GMm}{s^2} = \frac{gR^2m}{s^2} \qquad \text{(substituting } GM = gR^2)$$

$$= \frac{mgR^2}{s^2}$$

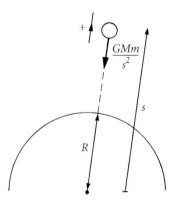

Figure 1.5

(ii) Take the positive direction (increasing s) upwards. The force is acting downwards, hence the negative sign when applying the equation of motion.

$$-\frac{mgR^2}{s^2} = mv\frac{\mathrm{d}v}{\mathrm{d}s}$$

The $v\dfrac{dv}{ds}$ form for acceleration is used since the problem involves distances and velocities.

Dividing by m and separating the variables gives

$$\int v\,dv = -\int \frac{gR^2}{s^2}\,ds$$

$$\Rightarrow \qquad \frac{1}{2}v^2 = \frac{gR^2}{s} + c$$

s is the distance from the centre of the Earth, so $v = u$ when $s = R$, giving
$c = \frac{1}{2}u^2 - gR$.

$$\Rightarrow \qquad \frac{1}{2}v^2 = \frac{gR^2}{s} + \frac{1}{2}u^2 - gR.$$

$v = 0$ when $s = h + R$ gives

$$\frac{1}{2}u^2 = gR - \frac{gR^2}{h+R} \qquad\qquad\qquad ①$$

$$u^2 = \frac{2gRh}{h+R}.$$

(iii) When $h = R$, $u^2 = gR$

$$\Rightarrow \qquad u = \sqrt{gR} = 7920. \quad \longleftarrow \quad \boxed{R = 6400 \times 10^3 \text{ in metres.}}$$

The launch speed is approximately $7.9\,\text{km s}^{-1}$.

(iv) $\dfrac{gR^2}{h+R} \to 0$ as $h \to \infty$, so equation ① gives $\dfrac{1}{2}u^2 \to gR$ for large h.

In order never to return, the minimum launch speed is $\sqrt{2gR} = 11\,200\,\text{ms}^{-1}$.

This is $11.2\,\text{km s}^{-1}$. For obvious reasons, this value of u is known as the *escape velocity*.

An alternative solution using energy methods is given in Example 1.6 on pages 23 to 24.

ACTIVITY 1.2   **Escape velocity**

Assume that all of a group of planets, including the Earth, can be modelled as spheres of equal densities.

(i) Show that the escape velocity from the surface of a planet is proportional to the radius.

(Remember: $g = \dfrac{GM}{R^2}$.)

(ii) What would be the escape velocity from the surface of a planet with a radius $\frac{1}{1000}$th that of the Earth's?

(iii) Many asteroids (minor planets between the orbits of Mars and Jupiter) are only a few kilometres in radius.

Could you hit a tennis ball into space from the surface of an asteroid?

Could you jump off into space?

Variation of *g* on the Earth's surface

The apparent weight of a body varies slightly at different parts of the Earth's surface. One reason is that the Earth is rotating. Unless you are at one of the poles, you are rotating in a circle round the Earth's axis and a small part of the gravitational force supplies the central acceleration for circular motion. You would otherwise be thrown into space. This has nothing to do with gravity but does affect what is measured as *g*.

In addition, the Earth is not spherical but bulges at the equator. The equatorial radius is about 1 part in 300 greater than the polar radius. Thus someone at the equator is further from the centre than someone at a pole.

These effects combine to make *g* about 0.5% less at the equator than at the poles.

 How much faster does a pendulum swing at the poles?

Historical note

The radius of the Earth has been known since ancient times; the first reasonable estimate was by Eratosthenes (born in 276 BC). He was curator of the library at Alexandria and measured the elevation of the sun at noon on midsummer day to be about 7°. Due south at Syene (now Aswan), at the same time, on the same day, the sun was known to be overhead. So a 7° arc along the circumference of the Earth corresponded to the known distance between Alexandria and Syene. Thus the circumference of the Earth and hence its radius could be estimated.

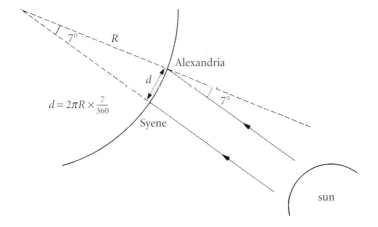

Figure 1.6

The value of g can be measured directly so, if the gravitational constant G can be determined, the mass of the Earth can be deduced using $g = \dfrac{GM}{R^2}$. Henry Cavendish, a brilliant but reclusive British physicist, performed a classic experiment to measure G in 1798. A rod with lead weights at each end was suspended on a fine fibre. When large weights are brought near the suspended ones, the tiny gravitational attraction causes a minute twist of the rod. This can be amplified and measured by the movement of a beam of light reflected from a mirror attached to the fibre.

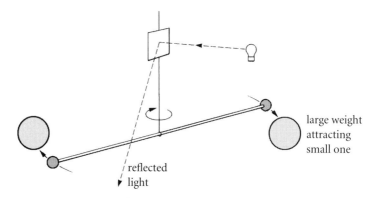

large weight
attracting
small one

reflected
light

Figure 1.7

1 The gravitational acceleration on a body at a distance r from the centre of a uniform sphere of mass M has magnitude $\dfrac{GM}{r^2}$, where G is the gravitational constant.

(i) What are the dimensions of G?

(ii) Assuming the Earth can be modelled as a perfect sphere of mass M and radius R, write down an expression for a_h, the acceleration due to gravity at a distance h above the Earth's surface.

What symbol is normally used for a_0?

(iii) Show that

$$a_h = g\left(1 + \frac{h}{R}\right)^{-2}.$$

(iv) Hence show that when h is small compared to the radius of the Earth, so that $\left(\dfrac{h}{R}\right)^2$ is negligible,

$$a_h = g\left(1 - \frac{2h}{R}\right).$$

(v) Given that the radius of the Earth is about 6400 km, by what percentage does gravitational acceleration differ from g at a height of 50 km?

2 The gravitational acceleration on a body at a distance x from the centre of the Earth has magnitude $\dfrac{k}{x^2}$, where k is a constant. An artificial satellite is in a circular orbit of radius r about the centre of the Earth.

(i)   Show that $k = gR^2$, where R is the radius of the Earth and g has its usual significance.

(ii) Write down the gravitational acceleration of the satellite in terms of R, r and g.

Hence show that the time T taken for the satellite to orbit the Earth is given by

$$T = \frac{2\pi}{R}\sqrt{\frac{r^3}{g}}$$

(iii) Show that a satellite in circular orbit with a period of 24 hours (a geosynchronous satellite) will be about 36 000 km above the Earth's surface. (Take g as $9.8\,\text{ms}^{-2}$ and the radius of the Earth as 6400 km.)

3 A meteor of mass m is attracted towards the moon by a gravitational force $\dfrac{mk}{r^2}$, where k is a constant and r is the distance of the meteor from the centre of the moon.

The meteor initially has negligible velocity and is at a distance R above the moon's surface, where R is the radius of the moon. It then falls directly towards the moon.

(i)   Starting from Newton's second law, find the velocity of the meteor when it smashes into the surface, in terms of k and R.

(ii) The radius of the moon is 1750 km and the gravitational acceleration at the surface is $1.6\,\text{ms}^{-2}$.

Using this information, find the value of k (in SI units) and hence find the actual final velocity of the meteor.

4 A body of unit mass *inside* a uniform sphere at a distance r from its centre O experiences a gravitational attraction towards the centre of $\dfrac{GM_r}{r^2}$, where G is the gravitational constant and M_r is the mass of material inside the sphere of radius r, (In other words it is as if the body were on the surface of a sphere of radius r, all the matter further from the centre than r will have no net gravitational effect on the body.)

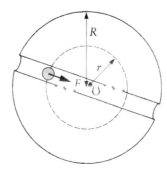

The body experiences net gravitational force due only to the mass in the sphere of radius r.

Suppose a straight tube could be drilled right through the Earth, modelled as a uniform sphere of radius R and total mass M. A ball is dropped into the tube at the surface of the Earth.

(i) Work out the mass of a sphere of the Earth of radius r, in terms of R, M and r.

(ii) Write down an expression for the gravitational force on the ball when at a distance r from the centre.

(iii) Hence show that the ball will oscillate with simple harmonic motion with an amplitude equal to the radius of the Earth. Determine the period.

5 A missile is projected vertically, with speed u, from the Earth's surface with the aim of reaching the moon. The missile travels in a straight line from the Earth to the moon (whose motion is ignored). It is assumed that the only forces acting on the missile during its journey are the gravitational attractions of the Earth and moon. M_e and M_m denote the masses of the Earth and moon, R the radius of the Earth and d the distance between the centres of the Earth and moon. The gravitational attraction between two bodies masses m_1 and m_2 may be taken as $\dfrac{Gm_1m_2}{r^2}$, where r is the distance between their centres and G is the gravitational constant.

(i) Write down an expression for the acceleration of the missile when it has reached a point a distance x from the Earth's centre (i.e. height $x - R$ above the Earth's surface).

(ii) Show that the acceleration is zero when

$$x = \frac{d}{1 + \sqrt{\dfrac{M_m}{M_e}}}$$

(iii) Integrate your expression for the acceleration to derive an expression for the velocity of the particle as a function of the distance x.

(iv) Explain how you would calculate the minimum launch speed required to reach the moon. (You need not actually derive this.)

Work, energy and impulse with variable forces

The concepts of work, energy and impulse are very valuable in the context of variable forces. In particular, the principle of conservation of mechanical energy, which has been previously used to solve problems without having to calculate acceleration explicitly, often enables you to solve variable-force problems which would not be easily dealt with by integration.

You have already partly covered this topic. *Mechanics 2* gave the definition of the impulse of a variable force and *Mechanics 3* showed how to calculate the work against the tension when stretching an elastic string. This section reviews the definitions of work, energy and impulse when variable forces are involved and applies them to the resistive and gravitational forces you have already met in this chapter.

Work done by a variable force

When a body moves a short distance δs along a line solely under the action of a parallel force F, you know that the force has done *an element of work* $\delta W = F\,\delta s$. When the force is *varying*, the total work is the sum of all these elements, that is

$$\int F\,\mathrm{d}s\,.$$

Note

You may not be satisfied with this and similar informal arguments. A more rigorous treatment is as follows.

Assuming the force increases from F to $F + \delta F$ as the body moves; then

$$F\delta s < \delta W < (F + \delta F)\delta s$$

$$\Rightarrow \qquad F < \frac{\delta W}{\delta s} < F + \delta F$$

As $\delta s \to 0$, $\delta F \to 0$ and $\dfrac{\delta W}{\delta s} \to \dfrac{\mathrm{d}W}{\mathrm{d}s}$, hence $\dfrac{\mathrm{d}W}{\mathrm{d}s} = F$.

By integration, the total work done over the period of the motion is $W = \int F\,\mathrm{d}s$.

In *Mechanics 3*, $\int F\,\mathrm{d}s$ was used to find the work done in extending an elastic string, of stiffness k, by an amount s. When extended by x, the tension in the string is, by Hooke's law, kx. Hence the total work starting from zero extension is

$$\int_0^s kx\,\mathrm{d}x = \tfrac{1}{2}ks^2$$

which is the elastic energy in a stretched spring.

Work done = increase in kinetic energy

You have seen this important result, which follows from Newton's second law

$$F = ma = mv\frac{dv}{ds},$$

Separating the variables and taking u and v as the starting and finishing velocities respectively, you get

$$\int F\,ds = \int mv\,dv$$

$$= \tfrac{1}{2}mv^2 - \tfrac{1}{2}mu^2$$

work done by force = increase in kinetic energy

EXAMPLE 1.5

A particle of mass 1 kg moves along a line with a velocity v ms^{-1} under the influence of a resistive force of magnitude kv^2 N, where k is a constant.

Initially, the velocity of the particle is 10 ms^{-1} and the force continues to act until the particle has slowed down to 5 ms^{-1}.

(i) Use kinetic energy considerations to write down the work done by the resistive force.

(ii) Solve the equation of motion of the particle and express the displacement x in terms of v.

Hence show that the particle travels a distance $s = \dfrac{1}{k}\ln 2$ m while the force acts.

(iii) From part **(ii)** express v and hence F in terms of x.

Hence confirm by integration the result obtained in part **(i)**.

SOLUTION

(i) Work done = final K.E. − initial K.E.

$$= \tfrac{1}{2}\times 5^2 - \tfrac{1}{2}\times 10^2 \text{ J}$$

$$= -37.5 \text{ J}$$

This is negative because the force is in the opposite direction to the displacement.

(ii) Applying $F = ma$ with $m = 1$ and $a = v\dfrac{dv}{dx}$, where x is displacement

$$-kv^2 = v\frac{dv}{dx}$$

Figure 1.8

Separating the variables gives

$$-k\int dx = \int \frac{dv}{v}$$

$$\Rightarrow \qquad -kx = \ln v + c$$

When $x = 0$, $v = 10$, hence $c = -\ln 10$. So

$$-kx = \ln v - \ln 10$$

$$= -\ln \frac{10}{v}$$

$$\Rightarrow \qquad x = \frac{1}{k}\ln\frac{10}{v} \qquad \qquad \qquad \text{①}$$

When $v = 5$ (final velocity)

$$x = s = \frac{1}{k}\ln 2$$

(iii) Making v the subject in ① gives $v = 10\,e^{-kx}$. Therefore

$$F = -kv^2$$

$$= -100k\,e^{-2kx}$$

Work done is $\int F\,dx$:

$$\int F\,dx = \int_0^s -100k\,e^{-2kx}\,dx$$

$$= 50\int_0^s -2k\,e^{-2kx}\,dx$$

$$= 50\left[e^{-2kx}\right]_0^s$$

Now $s = \frac{1}{k}\ln 2$ so

$$e^{-2ks} = e^{-2\ln 2}$$

$$= e^{\ln\frac{1}{4}}$$

$$\Rightarrow \qquad e^{-2ks} = \tfrac{1}{4}$$

Thus the work done $= 50(\tfrac{1}{4} - 1)$

$$= -37.5$$

This is -37.5 J, as in part **(i)**.

Force–distance graph

Note that if you plot force against distance (as in figure 1.9), the work done $\int F \, dx$ is the area under the graph.

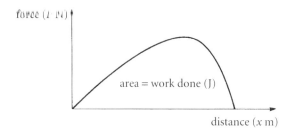

Figure 1.9

Simple harmonic motion by the energy method

In *Mechanics 3*, you investigated the spring–mass oscillator: a particle of mass m suspended on a spring oscillating vertically about its equilibrium position. You can derive the same results by the energy method.

A particle of mass m is suspended from a spring of natural length l and stiffness k. Without referring to the equilibrium position, write down an expression for the total energy when the spring is extended by x and moving with velocity v.

The total energy is constant throughout the motion. Differentiate the energy equation with respect to x and show that the mass oscillates with simple harmonic motion. Deduce the equilibrium position *from* the simple harmonic motion equation.

Gravitational potential energy

For a body moving near the Earth's surface, the work done by the gravitational force is often expressed as the change in the *potential energy* of the body. When a body of mass m rises a distance h, the work done *against* the gravitational force, mg, is mgh and you know this is the increase in potential energy of the body.

When the gravitational force *changes*, such as in the case of a missile launched from the Earth's surface into space, the work done is obtained by integration as follows.

The gravitational force on a body of mass m at a distance r_1 from a body of mass M is

$$F = -\frac{GMm}{r_1^2}.$$

The positive direction will be that of increasing r, hence the minus sign. Suppose a body of mass m is pulled away from a distance r_1 to a distance r_2 (as in figure 1.10), what work is done *against* the gravitational force?

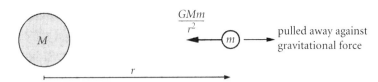

Figure 1.10

The work done is

$$\int_{r_1}^{r_2} -F\,dr = \int_{r_1}^{r_2} \frac{GMm}{r^2}\,dr$$

$$= \left[-\frac{GMm}{r} \right]_{r_1}^{r_2}$$

$$= \frac{GMm}{r_1} - \frac{GMm}{r_2}$$

This is positive $(r_2 > r_1)$, since increasing the separation between the bodies involves positive work against the gravitational force.

Just as in the case of constant gravitation, the *increase in potential energy* is defined as the work done against the force. With this type of motion, the zero level of potential energy is normally taken at infinity so r_1 is infinite. Then the gravitational potential energy of a body of mass m at a distance r from a body of mass M is defined as the work done in bringing them together from infinity,

namely $-\dfrac{GMm}{r}$ $\qquad (r = r_2 < r_1)$.

The work done against gravitation in moving a spacecraft away from a planet is thus the increase in potential energy, which according to the formula depends only on the initial and final values of r. And since

work done against force = loss in kinetic energy

it follows once more that

gain in potential energy = loss in kinetic energy

The following example shows the use of gravitational potential energy on the problem solved in Example 1.4 using the equation of motion.

EXAMPLE 1.6

A ballistic missile, fired vertically from the Earth's surface with an initial velocity of u just reaches a height h.

Using energy methods, derive an expression giving u^2 in terms of R (the radius of the Earth), g and h. Assume the gravitational acceleration at a distance r from the centre of the Earth is $\dfrac{GM}{r^2}$, where $GM = gR^2$.

SOLUTION

At launch, the kinetic energy of the missile is $\frac{1}{2}mu^2$ and its potential energy is $-\dfrac{GMm}{R}$. At the missile's highest point, its velocity is zero and since it is a distance $(R + h)$ from the centre of the Earth, the potential energy is $-\dfrac{GMm}{R+h}$.

So, using the principle of conservation of energy:

loss in kinetic energy = gain in potential energy

$$\frac{1}{2}mu^2 = GMm\left(-\frac{1}{R+h}+\frac{1}{R}\right)$$

$$= GMm\left(\frac{h}{R(R+h)}\right)$$

$$\Rightarrow \qquad u^2 = \frac{2gRh}{(R+h)} \qquad \text{since } GM = gR^2.$$

This is the result obtained previously on page 14.

Note

Conservative forces

It is shown above that the work done against the gravitational force *depends only on the initial and final position of the body*. This means that when the body returns to its starting point, no *net* work has been done, so the kinetic energy will be the same as before. That is, the force conserves the total mechanical energy. Forces which have this property are known as *conservative*, a term you met in *Mechanics 2*. It can be shown that conservation of mechanical energy is equivalent to the fact that the work done is dependent only on the initial and final positions.

Potential energy is associated only with conservative forces. The gravitational force, the electrical force between charged particles, the tension in a spring (obeying Hooke's law) – these are all examples of conservative forces. Frictional forces and the forces involved in non-elastic collisions are not conservative. They are known as *dissipative* as they result in a reduction of the total mechanical energy.

Power with variable forces

As you know from *Mechanics 2*, power is defined as the rate at which work is done. The definition is independent of whether or not the force is varying.

$$P = \frac{\mathrm{d}W}{\mathrm{d}t} \qquad \Rightarrow \qquad W = \int P\,\mathrm{d}t$$

where the integration is performed over the total time period. This implies that the area under the power–time graph (see figure 1.11) is equal to the work done.

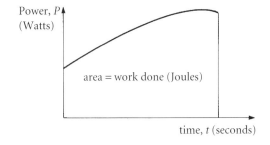

Power, P (Watts)

area = work done (Joules)

time, t (seconds)

Figure 1.11

Power = force × velocity

You have seen that $F = \dfrac{dW}{ds}$, where W is the work done. Hence by the chain rule

$$\frac{dW}{dt} \times \frac{dt}{ds} = F$$

$$\Rightarrow \qquad \frac{dW}{dt} = F\frac{ds}{dt}$$

Therefore, $\qquad P = Fv$

where v is the velocity of the body on which F acts.

This is a familiar result. Note that *constant power does not imply constant force*. When a car engine exerts a thrust of F N and the car is travelling with a speed v, the rate of working, i.e. power, is Fv Js^{-1}. If the power is constant, and v varies then F must vary.

EXAMPLE 1.7

When working at a constant power of 2.5 kW against a resistance proportional to the square of its speed, the maximum speed a vehicle can attain on a level road is 50 ms^{-1}. If the vehicle accelerates from rest under the same conditions, how far does it travel before it attains half the maximum speed? The mass of the vehicle is 1500 kg.

SOLUTION

The power is 2500 W = force × velocity, so the engine's driving force has a magnitude of $\dfrac{2500}{\text{velocity}}$.

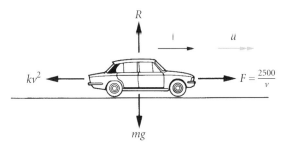

Figure 1.12

When the speed is v ms^{-1} and the resistance is kv^2 N, Newton's second law gives

$$\frac{2500}{v} - kv^2 = 1500a \qquad \text{①}$$

The maximum speed of 50 ms^{-1} occurs when the acceleration is zero. So

$$\frac{2500}{50} = k(50)^2$$

$$\Rightarrow \qquad k = \frac{1}{50}$$

Substituting this value of k in ① and using $a = v\dfrac{\mathrm{d}v}{\mathrm{d}x}$ since x is required gives

$$\frac{2500}{v} - \frac{v^2}{50} = 1500v\frac{\mathrm{d}v}{\mathrm{d}x}$$

$$\Rightarrow \qquad 125\,000 - v^3 = 75\,000v^2\frac{\mathrm{d}v}{\mathrm{d}x}$$

This can be solved by separating the variables and integrating.

$$\int \mathrm{d}x = \int \frac{75\,000v^2}{125\,000 - v^3}\,\mathrm{d}v$$

> This integral has been evaluated by inspection but could be found by substituting $z = 125\,000 - v^3$.

$$\Rightarrow \qquad x = -\frac{75\,000}{3}\ln\!\left(125\,000 - v^3\right) + c$$

$$x = 0 \text{ when } v = 0 \Rightarrow c = 25\,000\ln 125\,000$$

so $\qquad x = 25\,000\ln\!\left(\dfrac{125\,000}{125\,000 - v^3}\right)$

when $\quad v = 25, \quad x = 3338.$

The distance is therefore approximately 3.34 km.

Impulse of a variable force

For a constant force, the *impulse* is force $\times$ time for which it acts.

When the force varies, the impulse over a small time interval δt is $F\,\delta t$, and so the total impulse over a period is defined as $\int F\,\mathrm{d}t$ (see figure 1.13).

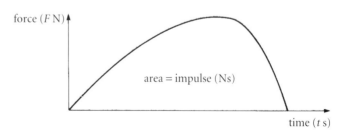

Figure 1.13

Over a period T in which the velocity changes from U to V

$$\int_0^T F \, dt = \int_U^V m \frac{dv}{dt} dt$$

since $F = m\dfrac{dv}{dt}$

$$\int_0^T F \, dt = \int_U^V m \, dv$$

$$= mV - mU$$

when m is constant.

This is the result which you saw in *Mechanics 2*, that the *impulse of a force is equal to the change in momentum*. This applies even when the force is varying.

Any collision involves variable forces. When two snooker balls, A and B, collide, they are in contact for a very short time. During that time the force between them is not constant. It is zero just as they touch, builds up to a maximum while they deform slightly and then goes down to zero again as the balls rebound. But, by Newton's third law, the force of A on B is equal and opposite to that of B on A *at every moment*. So, if the total impulse on A is $\int F \, dt$, that on B is

$$\int -F \, dt = -\int F \, dt.$$

The sum of the impulses on A and on B is zero and so the total momentum change is zero. The principle of conservation of momentum applies even though forces are variable.

1 A particle of mass 3 kg initially at rest is subject to a force whose magnitude increases linearly with time from zero to 2 N over a period of 1 second. What is the kinetic energy of the particle at the end of this period?

2 An object of mass 10 kg is acted on by a force whose magnitude varies according to the distance from the starting point O, as shown in the graph. The force acts in a constant direction.

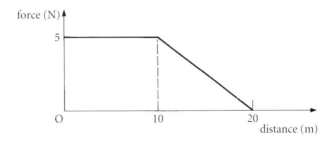

(i)   What work has been done by the force when the object reaches the point 20 m from O?

(ii) If the object starts from rest, what is its final speed?

(iii) What is its final momentum?

(iv) What is the total impulse of the force over the period?

3 An object of mass 10 kg begins at rest at O (see diagram), and is acted on by a force $F = 5 - \dfrac{s^2}{80}$, where s is the distance from O.

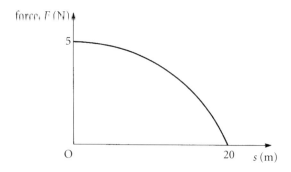

(i)   What is the speed when $s = 20$?

(ii) What is the total impulse of the force?

4 A car of mass 1000 kg is travelling on level ground at 5 ms^{-1} at time $t = 0$ when it begins to accelerate with its engine working at a constant 10 kW. Assume that its motion can be modelled neglecting friction and other forces.

(i)   Show that the thrust of the engine is inversely proportional to the speed of the car.

Write down the equation of motion involving velocity, v, and time, t.

(ii) Integrate and hence express v in terms of t.

Confirm that after 10 seconds the velocity is 15 ms^{-1}.

(iii) By writing v in the form $\dfrac{ds}{dt}$, integrate again and show that the distance travelled after time t is given by

$$s = \frac{1}{30}\left(20t + 25\right)^{\frac{3}{2}} - \frac{25}{6}.$$

(iv) Eliminate t between the equations derived in (ii) and (iii) and hence express s in terms of v.

(v)   Show that the result in part (iv) can be derived directly from another form of the equation of motion.

5 A catapult as shown projects a particle on a smooth horizontal surface. A light elastic string of natural length $8a$ and modulus of elasticity $2mg$ is attached to two points P and Q at a distance $8a$ apart on a horizontal table. A stone of mass m is attached to the mid-point, at a point D, drawn back a distance $3a$ to a point C and then released.

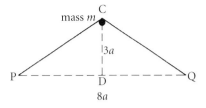

(i) What energy is stored in the elastic string when the mass is at point C?

(ii) Use conservation of energy to find the velocity of the stone when it reaches D.

(iii) The stone leaves the string when it reaches D, and is then acted on by a resistance of magnitude mkv, where v is the speed of the stone and k is a constant.

Show that it comes to rest at a distance $\dfrac{\sqrt{ga}}{k}$ from D.

6 The gravitational potential energy of a body of mass m at a distance r from the Earth's centre can be taken as $\dfrac{-R^2mg}{r}$, where R is the radius of the Earth and g is the gravitational acceleration at the surface.

(i) Give an expression for the total kinetic and potential energy of a missile of mass m fired with velocity u from the Earth's surface.

(ii) Use conservation of mechanical energy (neglecting forces other than gravity) to calculate the value of u for the missile to escape from the Earth completely. (Take g as 10 ms^{-2} and the Earth's radius as 6400 km.)

7 A particle of mass m, moving in the sun's gravitational field, at a distance x from the centre of the sun, experiences a force Gmx^{-2} (where G is a constant) directly towards the sun.

(i) Show that, if at some time $x = h$ and the particle is travelling directly away from the sun with speed V, then x cannot become arbitrarily large unless $V^2 \geqslant 2Gh^{-1}$.

(ii) A particle is initially motionless a great distance from the sun (of radius R). If, at some later time, it is at a distance h from the centre of the sun, how long after that will it take to fall into the sun?

8 A car of mass 800 kg moves along a straight horizontal road with its engine working at a constant rate of 40 kw. It starts from rest and after t seconds its speed is $v \text{ ms}^{-1}$. The resistance during this period is equal to $25v$ N.

(i) Show that $32v\dfrac{\mathrm{d}v}{\mathrm{d}t} = 1600 - v^2$.

(ii) Explain why the car cannot go faster than 40 ms^{-1}.

(iii) Express t in terms of v and find the time taken for the car to reach a speed of 35 ms^{-1} from rest.

9 The resistance to a car is proportional to the square of its speed. The car can cruise at a constant speed of $120\,\text{km}\,\text{h}^{-1}$ on the level exerting a power of $P\,\text{W}$, and it can coast (i.e. roll without power) down a hill of 1 in 20 at the same speed.

  (i) What would be its acceleration, at a power of $P\,\text{W}$, on the level at $60\,\text{km}\,\text{h}^{-1}$?

  (ii) If it maintains this power while accelerating from $60\,\text{km}\,\text{h}^{-1}$ to $90\,\text{km}\,\text{h}^{-1}$ on the level, find how far it would go during this acceleration. (Take g as $9.8\,\text{ms}^{-2}$.)

10 A train starts from a station. The tractive force exerted by the engine is at first constant and equal to F. However, after the speed attains the value u, the engine works at a constant rate P, where $P = Fu$. The mass of the engine and the train together is M. Forces opposing motion may be neglected.

  (i) Show that the engine will attain a speed v, with $v \geqslant u$, after a time since leaving the station of

$$\frac{M}{2P}\left(u^2 + v^2\right).$$

  (ii) Show that in this time it will have travelled a distance of

$$\frac{M}{6P}\left(2v^3 + u^3\right).$$

[O & C]

11 A motor car of mass m accelerates along a level straight road. Over a period, the engine works at a rate which can be modelled by $pv + q$, where v is the velocity of the car and p and q are positive constants. Its speed at the beginning of the period is $\frac{q}{p}$ and at the end of the period is $\frac{3q}{p}$. Resistance can be neglected.

  (i) What is the thrust on the engine when the car is moving with velocity v?

  (ii) Write down the equation of motion. Show that the variables can be separated to give

$$\int \frac{p}{m}\,\mathrm{d}t = \int \frac{pv}{pv+q}\,\mathrm{d}v.$$

  (iii) Show that the length of the period is

$$\left(2 - \ln 2\right)\frac{mq}{p^2}.$$

12 A road vehicle of mass M is initially at rest and then moves off in a straight line on a level road. The driving force is given by $MF(1 - e^{-at})$, where t is time and F and a are positive constants. The road resistance is given by Mbv, where b ($b \neq a$) is a positive constant and v is the vehicle speed.

(i) Write down the equation of motion of the vehicle.

(ii) Verify that

$$v = \frac{F}{b}\left\{1 - \frac{1}{a-b}\left(ae^{-bt} - be^{-at}\right)\right\}.$$

(iii) Determine the distance travelled, x, as a function of time.

(iv) Show that, for large values of t,

$$v \approx \frac{F}{b} \quad \text{and} \quad x \approx \frac{F}{b}\left\{t - \frac{a+b}{ab}\right\}.$$

[MEI]

13 The gravitational force on a particle of mass m at a distance s from the centre of the Earth is given by $\dfrac{mgR^2}{s^2}$ where R is the radius of the Earth and $s \geqslant R$.

The particle is projected vertically from the Earth's surface with an initial speed U, and the maximum height reached above the surface of the Earth is H. When it is at a height x above the surface of the Earth, the speed of the particle is v.

Resistance to motion and the rotation of the Earth can be neglected.

(i) Write down an equation for the upward motion of the particle. Hence show that

$$v^2 = U^2 - \frac{2gRx}{R+x}.$$

(ii) Deduce an expression for H.

(iii) Find an expression for the potential energy P at a height x, taking P to be equal to $-mgR$ when $x = 0$.

(iv) Explain carefully, with reference to both H and P, what happens

   (a) when $U^2 < 2gR$.

   (b) when $U^2 \geqslant 2gR$.

[MEI]

Resisted motion

A strong enough wind can blow you over; the force exerted by the air obviously depends on wind speed. You feel the same effect when you cycle or ski quickly – except that it is now called *air resistance* rather than wind. Any object moving through a fluid, such as a gas or a liquid, encounters a *resistive force* opposing its motion.

Experiments have shown that the air resistance on a moving object, such as a falling pebble, is approximately proportional to the square of its speed. The resistance is caused mainly because of the force required to push the particles of air into motion, in other words to change the momentum of the air particles. It is similar when the object is at rest and the wind blows against it – the force is produced by the loss of momentum of the air as it hits the object.

However, when the object is tiny (a particle of dust, for example), is slow-moving, or when it is moving through a liquid rather than a gas, then most of the resistive force is caused by *viscosity* – friction between layers of the liquid and between the liquid and the object. The viscous force (on a falling leaf or a lump of sugar dropped into a cup of coffee, for example) is directly proportional to speed. In general, motion through a fluid will be opposed by resistive forces which depend on a mixture of both *velocity* and *velocity squared*, but it is often the case that one dominates and the other can be ignored.

Terminal velocity

Imagine that a pebble of mass m, falling through the air, is subjected to a resistance proportional to the square of its speed, say kv^2, where k is a constant. This is a reasonable modelling assumption for such an object. The net downward force is $mg - kv^2$ (see figure 1.14). This is clearly a variable force. Applying Newton's second law at any instant gives

$$mg - kv^2 = m\frac{\mathrm{d}v}{\mathrm{d}t}.$$

$$a = \frac{\mathrm{d}v}{\mathrm{d}t} \quad + \quad \begin{array}{c} \uparrow kv^2 \\ \bigcirc \\ \downarrow mg \end{array}$$

Figure 1.14

You can get some idea of the behaviour of the pebble simply by looking at the differential equation. Initially v is zero, so the acceleration is g. Thus v will begin to increase. As v increases the acceleration $\dfrac{dv}{dt}$ gets smaller. As v^2 approaches $\dfrac{mg}{k}$, the left-hand side of the equation approaches zero, and therefore so does the acceleration. If v^2 ever becomes $\dfrac{mg}{k}$, the forces balance and there is no acceleration. The pebble would then continue at the speed $v = \sqrt{\dfrac{mg}{k}}$. This is known as its *terminal velocity*: it is the limiting speed that the pebble can reach. When an object is dropped from rest, its speed gets nearer and nearer to the terminal velocity but in theory does not quite achieve it, as the later worked examples show.

For situations that can be modelled by a resistive force proportional to v, for example a tiny raindrop falling in the air, Newton's second law gives

$$mg - cv = m\dfrac{dv}{dt}$$

where the resistive force is cv. You can see that in this case the terminal velocity has a value $\dfrac{mg}{c}$.

Modelling air resistance

Air resistance is quite significant in everyday situations. For example, a 2 cm diameter pebble dropped off a high cliff (don't do it!) has a terminal velocity of about 35 ms^{-1}, and the velocity is close to this after about 7 seconds.

❓ The graph shows how the speed of a granite pebble varies with time when it is dropped in air. The pebble has a diameter of 2 cm and a mass of 11.3 g.

What is the gradient of the graph at the origin?

How would you use the graph to estimate how far the stone has fallen before reaching 90% of its terminal velocity?

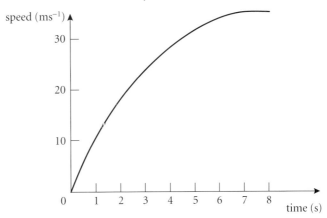

Figure 1.15

Modelling air resistance

A sphere of radius r metres moving through the air with a velocity $v\ \text{ms}^{-1}$ will encounter a resistive force of approximate magnitude

$$k_1 rv + k_2 r^2 v^2,$$

It is made up of two terms, one dependent on velocity, the other on velocity squared. In SI units, approximate values for k_1 and k_2 are respectively (3.1×10^{-4}) and 0.87, and the expression gives the resistive force in newtons.

(i) Investigate the air resistance on two pieces of stone of density $2.5\,\text{g cm}^{-3}$, both of which can be modelled as spheres. One is a pebble of radius $2\,\text{cm}$, the other a grain of radius $0.02\,\text{cm}$. For each object, use a computer graph-drawing package to draw a graph showing how the resistive force varies for values of the velocity between zero and the terminal velocity. This is when the force is equal to the weight of the stone.

(ii) At the terminal velocity, what is the relative importance of the v term as against the v^2 term in each case?
Do you think it is reasonable to ignore the v term when analysing the total motion of the pebble?

(iii) What about a $2\,\text{cm}$ radius puff-ball of mass $0.1\,\text{g}$?
Use the graph for the pebble to find its terminal velocity.
Is it still reasonable to ignore the v term?

Solving the resistive motion equations

To solve differential equations of resistive motion, write the acceleration in the form $\dfrac{dv}{dt}$ or $v\dfrac{dv}{ds}$, depending on whether you require *time* in the answer.

You can separate the variables and then integrate. You will find that many of the integrations result in logarithms or inverse trigonometrical functions.

EXAMPLE 1.8

A raindrop of mass m starts from rest and falls vertically. When falling with velocity v, it experiences a resistive force of magnitude kv.

(i) Express the terminal velocity V_T of the raindrop in terms of m, k and g.

(ii) Show that, if the raindrop starts from rest, its velocity v after time t is given by

$$v = V_T\left(1 - e^{-gt/V_T}\right)$$

(iii) Assuming the raindrop has a terminal velocity of $5\ \text{ms}^{-1}$, how long does it fall before it has 99% of the terminal velocity?
(Take g as $10\ \text{ms}^{-2}$.)

(iv) Derive an expression for the distance fallen in terms of time.

SOLUTION

(i) The forces on the raindrop are mg downwards and kv upwards. Applying Newton's second law at any instant:

$$mg - kv = ma.$$

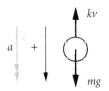

Figure 1.16

If the raindrop were moving at the terminal velocity, the acceleration would be zero, so

$$V_T = \frac{mg}{k}$$

(ii) It is helpful at this stage to divide the first equation by k and write $\frac{mg}{k} = V_T$ and $\frac{m}{k} = \frac{V_T}{g}$. Since time is required use $a = \frac{dv}{dt}$. The equation then becomes

$$V_T - v = \frac{V_T}{g} \times \frac{dv}{dt}$$

Now separate the variables and integrate.

$$\int \frac{dv}{\left(V_T - v\right)} = \int \frac{g}{V_T} dt$$

$$\Rightarrow \quad -\ln\left|V_T - v\right| = \frac{gt}{V_T} + c$$

$v = 0$ when $t = 0$ so $c = -\ln V_T$

> $V_T > v$ throughout the motion so $\left|V_T - v\right| = \left(V_T - v\right)$.

$$\Rightarrow \quad -\ln\left(V_T - v\right) = \frac{gt}{V_T} - \ln V_T$$

$$\Rightarrow \quad \ln\left[\frac{V_T - v}{V_T}\right] = -\frac{gt}{V_T}$$

$$\frac{V_T - v}{V_T} = e^{-gt/V_T}$$

which gives

$$v = V_T\left(1 - e^{-gt/V_T}\right)$$

or

$$v = V_T - V_T e^{-gt/V_T}. \qquad ①$$

> This makes it clear that, as you would expect, the velocity, v, is equal to the terminal velocity minus a small and decreasing amount.

(iii) When v is 99% of the terminal velocity, $\dfrac{v}{V_T} = 0.99$.

$$0.99 = 1 - e^{-gt/V_T} \qquad \textcircled{2}$$

$$= 1 - e^{-10t/5} \quad (g = 10,\ V_T = 5)$$

$$= 1 - e^{-2t}$$

$$\Rightarrow \qquad e^{-2t} = 0.01$$

$$e^{2t} = 100$$

> Note that the time taken to reach a given *percentage* of V_T does depend on the value of V_T. $V_T = 5$ was substituted in $\textcircled{2}$.

$$\Rightarrow \qquad t = \tfrac{1}{2}\ln 100 \doteq 2.3$$

The raindrop falls for 2.3 seconds before achieving 99% of V_T.

(iv) Having derived $\textcircled{1}$, write v as $\dfrac{ds}{dt}$ and integrate to get

$$\int ds = \int (V_T - V_T e^{-gt/V_T})\,dt$$

$$s = V_T t + \left(\frac{V_T^2}{g}\right) e^{-gt/V_T} + c$$

where c is the constant of integration.

Since $s = 0$ when $t = 0$, $c = -\dfrac{V_T^2}{g}$, so

$$s = V_T t - \frac{V_T^2}{g}(1 - e^{-gt/V_T}).$$

> The first term $V_T t$ is the distance that the raindrop would fall in a time t if travelling at speed V_T the whole time. s is always less than this.

Using a second-order equation

Example 1.8 involved integration twice, once to find v and again to find s. If you are not interested in v, and want s directly, you can express acceleration as $\dfrac{d^2s}{dt^2}$ and solve the second-order differential equation using the method described in *Differential Equations*. It has been included in Appendix 2 for interest.

Deciding on the positive direction

It is easy to get confused with the signs when writing down Newton's second law. Decide which is the direction in which you are measuring *positive displacement* and take this as your positive direction for *all variables*. A positive value of v means the body is moving in this direction. In the equation of motion, resistive forces will be in a direction opposite to that in which the body is moving. Thus, when the resistive force is proportional to velocity, write it as $-kv$ where k is a positive constant. If in fact the velocity is negative, the value of $-kv$ will be positive, still in the opposite direction to the motion. Your equation is correct whichever direction the body is actually moving in.

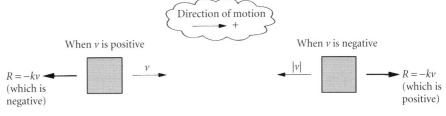

When *v* is positive

$R = -kv$
(which is
negative)

v

When *v* is negative

$|v|$

$R = -kv$
(which is
positive)

Figure 1.17

However, this does not work when the resistive force is proportional to v^2. You need different equations depending on which way the body is travelling and the two cases have to be considered separately as in the next example.

EXAMPLE 1.9

A heavy ball is retarded by air resistance which is modelled by kv^2, where $v\,\text{ms}^{-1}$ is the speed of the ball and k is a positive constant. When falling under gravity in air, its terminal velocity is $V\,\text{ms}^{-1}$.

(i) Write an expression for the total force on the ball when it is descending and hence derive an expression for V^2 in terms of k, g and the mass of the ball.

(ii) The ball is projected vertically upwards with an initial speed $u\,\text{ms}^{-1}$. Derive a differential equation, involving s and V, but not k, covering its ascent.

(iii) Show that, when $u = 50$ and $V = 100$, the ball reaches a height of almost 114 m.

SOLUTION

(i) Assume that the mass of the ball is m and the resistance is kv^2. When descending, the net downward force is $mg - kv^2$.

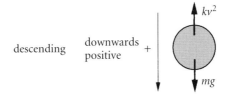

descending

downwards
positive

$+$

kv^2

mg

Figure 1.18

The terminal velocity, V, is obtained when the force is zero, so $mg = kV^2$.

$$\Rightarrow \qquad V^2 = \frac{mg}{k}$$

(ii) When ascending, both the weight and the air resistance are in the same direction. Take the positive direction as *upwards*, so the forces are negative and the initial velocity is positive.

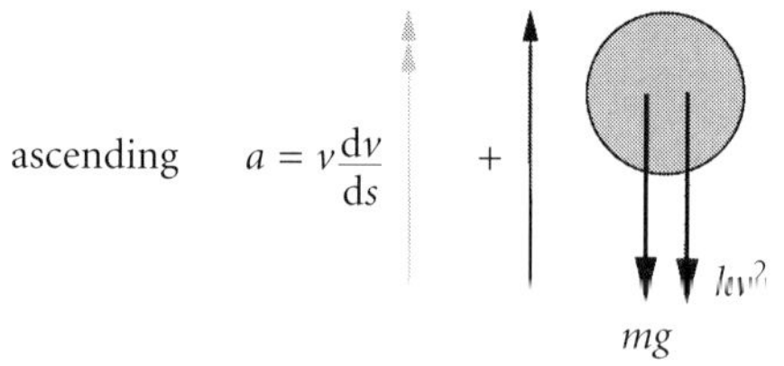

ascending $\quad a = v\dfrac{\mathrm{d}v}{\mathrm{d}s}$

mg

Figure 1.19

The equation of motion is then

$$-mg - kv^2 = mv\dfrac{\mathrm{d}v}{\mathrm{d}s}$$

$$-\dfrac{mg}{k} - v^2 = \dfrac{m}{k}v\dfrac{\mathrm{d}v}{\mathrm{d}s}$$

> For an equation in s write $a = v\dfrac{\mathrm{d}v}{\mathrm{d}s}$.

Substituting $\dfrac{mg}{k} = V^2$ gives

$$-V^2 - v^2 = \left(\dfrac{V^2}{g}\right)v\dfrac{\mathrm{d}v}{\mathrm{d}s}$$

$$v\dfrac{\mathrm{d}v}{\mathrm{d}s} = -\dfrac{g(V^2 + v^2)}{V^2}$$

(iii) Separating the variables and integrating gives

$$\int \dfrac{v\,\mathrm{d}v}{V^2 + v^2} = -\dfrac{g}{V^2}\int \mathrm{d}s$$

$$\dfrac{1}{2}\ln\left(V^2 + v^2\right) = -\dfrac{gs}{V^2} + c$$

If $v = u$ when $s = 0$, $c = \tfrac{1}{2}\ln(V^2 + u^2)$

$$\Rightarrow \quad \dfrac{gs}{V^2} = \dfrac{1}{2}\ln\left(V^2 + u^2\right) - \dfrac{1}{2}\ln\left(V^2 + v^2\right)$$

$$s = \dfrac{V^2}{2g}\ln\left(\dfrac{V^2 + u^2}{V^2 + v^2}\right)$$

> This is the general solution for s in terms of v.

When $v = 0$, $s = h$ so

$$h = \dfrac{V^2}{2g}\ln\left(\dfrac{V^2 + u^2}{V^2}\right)$$

> It is useful to check the dimensions. The expression $\ln\left(\dfrac{V^2 + u^2}{V^2}\right)$ is dimensionless so, on the right-hand side, $\dfrac{V^2}{2g}$ gives
> $$\dfrac{(\mathrm{LT}^{-1})^2}{\mathrm{LT}^{-2}} =$$
> $\mathrm{L}^2\mathrm{T}^{-2}\mathrm{L}^{-1}\mathrm{T}^2 = \mathrm{L}$, as required.

Substituting the values $V = 100$, $u = 50$ given in the question:

$$h = \dfrac{100^2}{2g}\ln 1.25 = 113.8$$

The ball reaches a height of 113.8 m.

Can a body descending under air resistance start off with a speed *greater* than the terminal velocity? How? What happens subsequently?

When a ball is thrown up in the air, does it take longer to go up or come down? Bear in mind that energy is dissipated by the air resistance and consider the velocity at corresponding points on the way up and the way down.

Historical note

The first thorough treatment of the motion of bodies in a resisting medium was given by Newton who devoted the second of the three books of his master work *Philosophiae Naturalis Principia Mathematica* (first edition 1687) to this topic. He considered motion where the fluid resistance is proportional to the velocity, the square of the velocity and a combination of the two. He also investigated the physical causes of fluid resistance.

Terminal velocity under resistive force was an important part of R.A. Millikan's classic experiment in 1896 to measure the charge on an electron (the smallest quantum of charge). He observed tiny charged droplets of oil rising or falling in an electric field and was able to measure the terminal velocity very accurately. The field causes an electric force on the charged particle in addition to the gravitational force and viscous force of the air. By observing, over many hours, the terminal velocity of the same droplet using different values of the electric field, Millikan was able to eliminate various other unknown quantities (e.g. the droplet's mass) and calculate the charge on the droplet. Such measurements on hundreds of droplets showed that the charge was always an integer multiple of the smallest charge: the charge on an electron.

EXERCISE 1D

1 The resistance to a cork of mass 10 g falling in air with velocity $v \, \text{ms}^{-1}$ can be modelled as $kv^2 \, \text{N}$, where k is constant.

(i) Write down the equation of motion and hence deduce an expression for the terminal velocity in terms of k.

(ii) Find the value of k, given that the terminal velocity is $15 \, \text{ms}^{-1}$.

(iii) At what speed is the resistive force equal to half the weight of the cork?

2 In an experiment with Millikan's oil-drop apparatus, the resistive force on a spherical oil droplet of radius r m with a velocity $v \, \text{ms}^{-1}$ can be modelled as $3.1 \times 10^{-4} \, rv \, \text{N}$. The density of the oil is $800 \, \text{kg m}^{-3}$.

(i) Find the mass of an oil drop of radius 1 micron ($10^{-6} \, \text{m}$).

(ii) Write down the equation of motion for such an oil drop falling under gravity. Hence determine the terminal velocity.

(iii) A droplet moving at its terminal velocity is observed to take 20 seconds to fall 5 mm. What is its radius? (Take $g = 9.8 \, \text{ms}^{-2}$.)

3 A car of mass m kg, moving at 25 ms^{-1} on a level road, runs out of petrol and coasts to a lay-by 0.6 km further on. It is acted on by a resistive force of magnitude $\dfrac{m(v^2+1)}{200}$ N, where $v \text{ ms}^{-1}$ is the car's speed. Find the speed of the car when it reaches the lay-by.

4 Moira pushes herself off from the bank of a frozen pond with an initial speed $u \text{ ms}^{-1}$ and then slides across the ice until she stops. The horizontal force is a resistance of kv newtons, where $v \text{ ms}^{-1}$ is her velocity and k is a constant. Moira's mass is 40 kg.

  (i) Give Newton's second law for the motion, writing acceleration as $\dfrac{dv}{dt}$.

  (ii) Find Moira's speed after 1 second, in terms of u and k.

  (iii) Show that her speed reduces by the same proportion each second.

  (iv) Given that u is 5 and the resistance is $5v$ N, find the distance she has travelled after 5 seconds.

  (v) Show that she will not go further than 40 m.

5 A sphere of radius R m dropped in water is resisted by a viscous force $6\pi R\eta v$ N, where $v \text{ ms}^{-1}$ is the velocity of the sphere and η is the coefficient of viscosity. Also according to Archimedes' principle, a body immersed in a fluid receives an upthrust equal to the weight of fluid displaced by the volume of the body. Experiments are performed by releasing glass marbles in the water. ρ_g denotes the density of glass and ρ_w the density of water.

  (i) Find the weight of water which a marble displaces and hence write the equation of motion for the marble as it descends.

  (ii) Show that the terminal velocity V_T has the value

$$\left(\frac{2R^2g}{9\eta}\right)(\rho_g - \rho_w)g$$

  and that the equation of motion may be written

$$V_T - v = \left(\frac{2R^2\rho_g}{9\eta}\right)\frac{dv}{dt}$$

  (iii) Taking ρ_g as 3000 kg m^{-3}, ρ_w as 1000 kg m^{-3}, the value of η as 1 in SI units, and g as 10 ms^{-2}, find the terminal velocity of a 1 cm diameter marble.

  Deduce the terminal velocity for a 2 cm diameter marble.

  (iv) How long does it take for the 1 cm marble to reach 99% of its terminal velocity?

6 A skier is descending a slope 30° to the horizontal against resistive forces proportional to her speed. The terminal velocity under these conditions is 20 ms^{-1}. She has managed to reach this velocity when she arrives at the bottom and begins to ascend at an angle of 2°. She continues against the same type of resistive forces (without pushing with her sticks) until she stops.

(i) If the resistive forces have magnitude kv, and the skier has mass m, derive the terminal velocity for the descent, and hence express k in terms of g and m.

(ii) Once the skier starts to ascend, what is the total force down the slope? Express this in terms of g, m and her velocity v.

(iii) Write down the equation of motion of the skier up the slope and show that she comes to a halt just over 11 seconds after beginning to ascend.

(iv) How far up the slope does she travel?

7 A ball bearing released from rest in a fluid falls under gravity. When its distance below the point of release is x, its speed, v, satisfies the equation

$$-\frac{gx}{V} = v + V \ln\left(1 - \frac{v}{V}\right) \text{ where } V \text{ is a constant.}$$

(i) Find $\dfrac{dv}{dx}$.

(ii) By writing acceleration as $v\dfrac{dv}{dx}$, show that the motion can be explained by assuming a resistive force proportional to velocity (assuming no buoyancy effects). Show that V is the terminal velocity under these conditions.

(iii) Show that the velocity after time t is given by

$$v = V(1 - e^{-t/t_0})$$

where t_0 is the time which the ball bearing would take to reach velocity V if falling under gravity with no resistance.

8 A ball of mass m is thrown vertically upwards with an initial speed U. The air resistance, proportional to the square of the speed of the ball, is such that in free fall under gravity, the ball would reach a terminal speed V.

(i) Show that when the particle is moving upwards with speed v, the retardation is of magnitude $g\left(1 + \dfrac{v^2}{V^2}\right)$.

(ii) Show that the ball reaches a maximum height of $\dfrac{V^2}{2g}\ln\left(1 + \dfrac{U^2}{V^2}\right)$.

(iii) Find the speed with which it returns to its starting point.

(iv) Find an expression for the speed of the ball as a function of time during its ascent.

[MEI, adapted]

9 A body of mass m kg is dropped vertically into a deep pool of liquid. Once in the liquid, it is subject to gravity, an upward buoyancy force of $\frac{6}{5}$ times its weight, and a resistive force of $2mv^2$ N opposite to its direction of travel when it is travelling at v ms^{-1}.

(i) Show that, however large its initial speed, the body stops sinking less than $\frac{\pi}{4}$ seconds after it enters the pool.

(ii) Suppose now that the body enters the liquid with speed 1 ms^{-1}.
Show that the body descends to a depth of $\frac{1}{4}\ln 2$ m and that it returns to the surface with speed $\dfrac{1}{\sqrt{2}}$ ms^{-1}.

(iii) Show further that it returns at a time

$$\frac{\pi}{8} + \frac{1}{4}\ln\frac{(\sqrt{2}+1)}{(\sqrt{2}-1)}$$

Take the value of g to be 10 ms^{-2}.

[O & C]

10 In tests of a new engine for a sports car, the car is driven along a level road. The mass of the car is m and v is the speed of the car at time t. The driving force is equal to mav and the resistance to mbv^2, where a and b are constants. After a time t the car has travelled a distance x.

(i) Write down the differential equation for v that describes the motion of the car as a function of t.

Hence write down a differential equation for $\dfrac{dv}{dx}$.

(ii) Show that $v = \dfrac{a}{b} + Be^{-bx}$, where B is a constant.

Give interpretations of the quantities $\dfrac{a}{b}$ and $\dfrac{a}{b} + B$ in terms of the speed of the car.

At the start of a particular trial, the speed of the car increases from V to $2V$ as x increases from 0 to L, where $V < \dfrac{a}{2b}$.

(iii) Find B in terms of V, a and b. Show that $L = \dfrac{1}{b}\ln\left(\dfrac{\frac{a}{b}-V}{\frac{a}{b}-2V}\right)$.

Show further that the car has its maximum acceleration when $v = \dfrac{a}{2b}$ and that this occurs when it has moved a distance $\dfrac{1}{b}\ln\left(2 - \dfrac{2bV}{a}\right)$.

[MEI]

11 A light aircraft of total mass m has an engine which can develop maximum power P. When the aircraft is moving on a level runway at speed v the total resistance to motion is mkv^2 where k is a constant. In order to take off, the pilot holds the aircraft stationary at one end of the runway and releases the brakes when the engine reaches full power. The runway has length l. The aircraft moves a distance x to reach a speed v and the speed required for take-off is V_0.

(i) Write down a differential equation for the motion of the aircraft. Show that the equation can be written in the form

$$\frac{dv}{dx} = \frac{k\left(A^3 - v^3\right)}{v^2}, \qquad \text{where } A^3 = \frac{P}{mk}.$$

(ii) Hence show that

$$x = \frac{1}{3k}\ln\left(\frac{A^3}{A^3 - v^3}\right).$$

Give a physical interpretation of A, and deduce the minimum length of runway necessary for take-off.

(iii) Show that the work, W, done against the total resistance during take-off can be written

$$W = \int_0^{V_0} \frac{mv^4 dv}{A^3 - v^3}.$$

[You are not expected to evaluate this integral.]

(iv) By considering this integral as the area under a suitable curve, justify the following two statements.

(a) The final part of the take-off accounts for most of the energy loss.

(b) The energy loss decreases if the total load of the aircraft is reduced.

[MEI]

12 A golf ball of mass 0.04 kg lies at rest on a golf course. It is struck by a golf club which exerts upon it a force of magnitude $F = 5000\,(e^{-1000t} - e^{-2000t})$ newtons for a period $0 \leqslant t \leqslant 0.01$ second after which the ball and the club separate. Assume that the force acts along a straight line.

Find, correct to 3 significant figures,

(i) the magnitude of the maximum force exerted on the ball
(ii) the speed of the ball at the instant the ball and the club separate
(iii) the distance the ball travels while in contact with the club
(iv) the work done on the ball by the club.

[MEI]

13 The speed limiter on a test vehicle operates by reducing the driving force F as the speed increases. The force is given by

$$F = mk\left(A^2 - v^2\right),$$

where v is the speed, m the mass and k, A are constants.

When moving on level ground, the resistance to motion is Bmv^2, where B is a constant. The greatest speed that the vehicle can reach is V_0.

(i) Write down the equation of motion for the vehicle.

(ii) Show that $V_0^2 = \dfrac{kA^2}{k+B}$, and deduce that the equation of motion can be written as $\dfrac{dv}{dt} = c\left(V_0^2 - v^2\right)$, where $c = k + B$ and t is time.

The vehicle starts from rest at $t = 0$ and after a time t has moved a distance of x.

(iii) Show that the speed v at time t is given by

$$v = V_0 \left(\frac{e^{cV_0t} - e^{-cV_0t}}{e^{cV_0t} + e^{-cV_0t}} \right).$$

(iv) Hence, or otherwise, deduce an expression for x as a function of t.

[MEI]

ⓔ Vector forms

All the work in this chapter has been in one dimension but many of the expressions you have used have equivalent forms which can be used for working in two or three dimensions. These are given below for completeness.

- In vector form, Newton's second law is $\mathbf{F} = m\mathbf{a}$. Two-dimensional problems can be solved by regarding this as two equations for the $\mathbf{i}$ and $\mathbf{j}$ directions.
- Work, impulse and power are defined for variable forces in vector form as follows.

Work done	$\int \mathbf{F} \cdot ds$
Impulse	$\int \mathbf{F}\, dt$
Power	$\mathbf{F} \cdot \mathbf{v}$

1 When a particle is moving along a line under a variable force F, Newton's second law gives a differential equation. It is generally solved by writing acceleration as

$$\frac{\mathrm{d}v}{\mathrm{d}t} \qquad \text{when } F \text{ is given as a function of time, } t$$

$$v\frac{\mathrm{d}v}{\mathrm{d}s} \qquad \text{when } F \text{ is given as a function of displacement, } s$$

$$\frac{\mathrm{d}v}{\mathrm{d}t} \text{ or } v\frac{\mathrm{d}v}{\mathrm{d}s} \qquad \text{when } F \text{ is given as a function of velocity, } v.$$

2 Where forces are conservative, variable force problems may be handled using the principle of conservation of energy.

3 A *resistive* force is opposite to the direction of motion, and its magnitude often depends on the speed: typically it is proportional to v or v^2.

4 The *terminal velocity* of a falling body is reached when the resistive force is balanced by the force of gravity.

5 The gravitational force between two particles is proportional to the product of their masses and inversely proportional to the square of the distance between them: $F = \dfrac{Gm_1m_2}{r^2}$.

6 Work, impulse and power are defined for variable forces as follows.

Work done	$\int F \, \mathrm{d}s$
Impulse	$\int F \, \mathrm{d}t$
Power	Fv

Variable mass

Plus ça change, plus c'est la même chose

Alphonse Karr

1 What causes the rocket to move?

2 A wagon is rolling freely along a level track at constant speed when it passes under a hopper which dumps coal into it. A short way further on, the bottom of the wagon opens up to allow the coal to drop out.

Assuming friction can be neglected, will the speed of the wagon at the end be greater than, less than or the same as at the beginning?

A rocket loses mass as it expels fuel. For example, each of the two launch rockets of Ariane 5 uses over 1.8 tonnes of fuel in just over 2 minutes. A falling raindrop may shrink because of evaporation or, when falling in mist, grow because of condensation. The motion of the rocket and that of the raindrop are affected not only by external forces but by the fact that their mass is changing. This chapter deals with such situations. The topic is usually called *variable mass* because you form an equation of motion referring to a system (e.g. the rocket) whose mass is changing. Of course, mass is not (normally) created or destroyed. The mass of the rocket indeed decreases but the lost mass is fuel expelled into space. As you will see, the velocity of this fuel is a crucial factor in the motion of the rocket.

Obtaining the equations of motion

In this chapter you will meet three types of problem in which the mass of an object changes continuously as it moves in a straight line.

- The object picks up stationary matter as it goes along, for example, a raindrop falling through a cloud.
- The object drops matter as it goes along, for example, a truck dropping tarmac on to a road.
- The object expels matter in order to accelerate, for example, a rocket.

The equation of motion depends on the situation and it is best to approach it from first principles using the momentum–impulse equation. In the next two sections you will see how this works in the first two situations. Rocket motion is covered later in the chapter.

Matter is picked up continuously from rest

The diagram shows an object of variable mass m which picks up a small mass, δm, over a short time, δt, during which its velocity changes from v to $v + \delta v$. There is an external force F acting in the direction of motion.

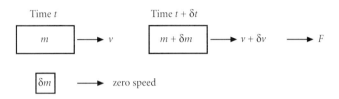

Figure 2.1

The gain in momentum is equal to the impulse of the force so:

$$(m + \delta m)(v + \delta v) - mv = F\delta t$$

$$\Rightarrow \quad m\delta v + \delta mv + \delta m\delta v = F\delta t$$

$$\Rightarrow \quad m\frac{\delta v}{\delta t} + \frac{\delta m}{\delta t}v + \frac{\delta m}{\delta t}\delta v = F.$$

$\delta v \to 0$ as $\delta t \to 0$, so the term $\frac{\delta m}{\delta t}\delta v$ disappears.

In the same way, any small variation in F over the time δt would also disappear, so the force, F, *does not have to be constant*. It could be mg for example.

In the limit as $\delta t \to 0$, this gives

$$m\frac{dv}{dt} + v\frac{dm}{dt} = F$$

$$\Rightarrow \quad \frac{d(mv)}{dt} = F.$$

This is the more general form of Newton's second law.

Force = rate of change of momentum

When m is constant it becomes the familiar

$$F = m\frac{dv}{dt} = ma.$$

When $F = 0$, the rate of change of momentum is zero, so momentum is conserved.

EXAMPLE 2.1

A canal barge is drifting without power under a hopper which is filling it with coal at a rate of r kg s^{-1}. The barge was initially moving with a velocity u ms^{-1} and its mass without the coal is M kg. The resistance of the water may be neglected.

(i) Denoting by m and v respectively the mass and velocity of the barge plus coal at time t, show that $m\dfrac{\mathrm{d}v}{\mathrm{d}t} = -v\dfrac{\mathrm{d}m}{\mathrm{d}t}$.

(ii) Show that the velocity of the barge t seconds after the coal begins to drop into the barge is given by $v = \dfrac{Mu}{(M+rt)}$.

(iii) Show that the distance travelled in this time is $S = \left(\dfrac{Mu}{r}\right)\ln\left(1 + \dfrac{r}{M}t\right)$.

SOLUTION

(i) Consider an instant at time t when the barge plus coal has mass m moving with velocity v. At a time δt later, a mass δm (whose initial velocity is zero) has been added, and the whole is now moving with a velocity $v + \delta v$. The change in momentum is

$$(m+\delta m)(v+\delta v) - mv = mv + v\delta m + m\delta v + \delta m\delta v - mv$$
$$= v\delta m + m\delta v + \delta m\delta v$$

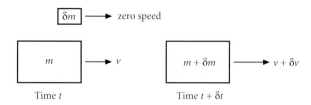

Figure 2.2

There is no net horizontal force, so there is no change in the total linear momentum of the coal plus barge: $v\delta m + m\delta v + \delta m\delta v = 0$.

Dividing through by δt and letting $\delta t \to 0$ gives

$$v\frac{\mathrm{d}m}{\mathrm{d}t} + m\frac{\mathrm{d}v}{\mathrm{d}t} = 0$$

$$\Rightarrow \qquad m\frac{\mathrm{d}v}{\mathrm{d}t} = -v\frac{\mathrm{d}m}{\mathrm{d}t}$$

$\delta m\dfrac{\delta v}{\delta t} \to 0$ as $\delta t \to 0$

As each δm of coal is added, its momentum increases from zero to $v\delta m$ so $v\dfrac{\mathrm{d}m}{\mathrm{d}t}$ is the rate of increase in momentum of the added mass. Hence the equation can be interpreted as

mass × acceleration = −(rate of increase of momentum from added mass).

Compare with $ma = -F$ and you can see that the effect of the coal being added is the same as a *resisting force of magnitude equal to the rate of increase in momentum* of the new coal.

(ii) This equation can be solved by separating the variables, but it is easier to go back to

$$m\frac{dv}{dt} + v\frac{dm}{dt} = 0$$

$$\Rightarrow \qquad \frac{d}{dt}(mv) = 0.$$

Integrating gives $mv = $ constant.

After time t, a mass rt of coal has been added. The mass is then $m = M + rt$. Hence

$$(M + rt)v = \text{constant} = Mu \quad (\text{since when } t = 0, v = u)$$

$$\Rightarrow \qquad v = \frac{Mu}{(M + rt)}.$$

> It is a good idea to check results by setting variables to extreme values. $r = 0$ implies no added mass, so the barge should continue to move at constant speed, hence $v = u$.

(iii) To work out distance travelled, v must be written as $\dfrac{ds}{dt}$.

$$\frac{ds}{dt} = \frac{Mu}{(M + rt)}$$

$$\Rightarrow \qquad s = \left(\frac{Mu}{r}\right)\ln(M + rt) + k$$

where k is the constant of integration. When $t = 0$, $s = 0$, giving

$$k = -\left(\frac{Mu}{r}\right)\ln M$$

$$s = \left(\frac{Mu}{r}\right)\left[\ln\left(M + rt\right) - \ln M\right]$$

$$= \left(\frac{Mu}{r}\right)\ln\left(1 + \frac{rt}{M}\right).$$

Matter is dropped continuously

You can work from first principles using a method similar to that on page 47 to deal with this situation. In this case the mass of the object decreases so δm is negative. However, it makes the problem easier to visualise if you use $|\delta m|$ as the mass dropped in time δt. Figure 2.3 summarises the situation.

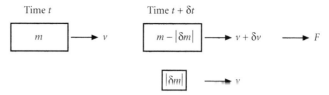

Time t Time $t + \delta t$

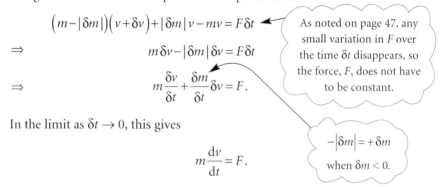

Figure 2.3

The gain in momentum is equal to the impulse of the force so:

$$\left(m - |\delta m|\right)\left(v + \delta v\right) + |\delta m| v - mv = F\delta t$$

As noted on page 47, any small variation in F over the time δt disappears, so the force, F, does not have to be constant.

$$\Rightarrow \qquad m\,\delta v - |\delta m|\,\delta v = F\delta t$$

$$\Rightarrow \qquad m\frac{\delta v}{\delta t} + \frac{\delta m}{\delta t}\delta v = F.$$

In the limit as $\delta t \to 0$, this gives

$$m\frac{dv}{dt} = F.$$

$-|\delta m| = +\delta m$ when $\delta m < 0$.

This looks more like the form $F = ma$, of Newton's second law.

When $F = 0$, the velocity is constant, but the momentum of the object decreases because its mass decreases. This is not a contradiction however, because the *total* momentum of the whole system is conserved. The mass which is dropped has momentum until it is acted on by some other external force.

The following example uses the same method with $|\delta m|$ written in terms of the time, δt.

EXAMPLE 2.2

A hopper truck containing gravel is moving along a horizontal railway line. The gravel is dropping out of the bottom at a constant rate of k kg s^{-1}.

(i) By considering the total linear momentum before and after a small interval of time from t to $t + \delta t$, show that the truck does not accelerate if there are no horizontal forces on it.

(ii) The truck is actually being pulled by a variable force F.

Derive the relationship between F and the acceleration of the truck when the mass of the truck plus gravel is m.

SOLUTION

(i) Denote by v the velocity of the truck at a time t when the mass of the truck and remaining gravel is m. The total linear momentum is thus mv.

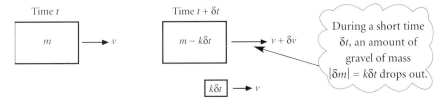

Figure 2.4

When the gravel begins dropping, its horizontal velocity is the same as that of the truck, i.e. v. The small change in this velocity over the time δt can be ignored when considering the momentum of this small mass. At the end of the period δt, the velocity of the truck will have increased to $v + \delta v$. The total momentum is now

$$(m - k\delta t)(v + \delta v) + vk\delta t = mv + m\delta v - k\delta t\delta v$$

> Note that the gravel dropping out retains its momentum until it hits the ground, of course, when other forces, not relevant to the problem, come into play.

The *increase* in linear momentum of the whole system is thus $m\delta v - k\delta t\ \delta v$. When there is no horizontal force, there is no change in momentum, so

$$m\delta v - k\delta t\delta v = 0.$$

Dividing through by the time interval δt gives

$$\frac{m\delta v}{\delta t} = k\delta v$$

In the limit as $\delta t \to 0$ and $\delta v \to 0$, the equation becomes $m\dfrac{dv}{dt} = 0$. The acceleration is zero.

(ii) When the truck is pulled by a force F, the impulse of the force over this period, $F\delta t$, is equal to the increase of momentum over the period.

$$F\delta t = m\delta v - k\delta t\delta v$$

$$\Rightarrow \qquad F = m\frac{\delta v}{\delta t} - k\delta v$$

In the limit as $\delta t \to 0$, and $\delta v \to 0$, the equation becomes $F = m\dfrac{dv}{dt}$.

You can see from the last two examples that, in variable mass problems, you have to be careful when using Newton's second law in the form $F = \dfrac{d}{dt}(mv)$. The momentum, mv, refers to the *total momentum of the system*. In Example 2.1, the coal has no linear momentum (in the direction of the barge motion) before it drops on to the barge, so that the momentum of the barge plus contents is equal to the momentum of the whole system. So, to solve part **(i)** of this problem, you could simply have written.

$$0 = \frac{d}{dt}(mv) = m\frac{dv}{dt} + v\frac{dm}{dt}.$$

But in Example 2.2, the gravel dropping off the truck retained its velocity, so applying $F = \frac{d}{dt}(mv)$ only to the truck would have been wrong. The lost mass still had its momentum. Of course, the gravel eventually hits the ground and loses its velocity, but then other forces are involved.

The following is another example where it is safe to apply the full form of Newton's second law. The mass being added to a moving object has no initial velocity and therefore $F = \frac{d}{dt}(mv)$ can be applied simply to the moving object.

EXAMPLE 2.3

A spherical droplet, initially of radius a, falls from rest under the influence of a gravitational field g, through a stationary light mist. The mass of the droplet increases due to the condensation of mist on its surface. Air resistance may be ignored.

(i) Denoting the mass and velocity of the droplet at any time t by m and v respectively, write down Newton's second law for the motion.

Deduce that the equation is consistent with an initial acceleration of g.

(ii) Given that the mass increases at a rate proportional to the instantaneous surface area of the droplet, show that its radius r increases linearly with time t, i.e. can be expressed in the form $r = ct + a$, where c is a constant.

(iii) Find v in terms of r, a, c and g.

(iv) Deduce that when $r \gg a$, the acceleration is approximately $\frac{g}{4}$.

SOLUTION

(i) The extra mass is at rest before condensing, therefore force = rate of change of momentum.

$$mg = \frac{d}{dt}(mv) = m\frac{dv}{dt} + v\frac{dm}{dt}$$

When $v = 0$, $mg = m\frac{dv}{dt} \Rightarrow \frac{dv}{dt} = g$.

The initial acceleration is g.

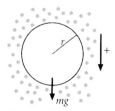

Figure 2.5

(ii) Mass of droplet = volume × density

$$m = \frac{4\pi r^3}{3}\rho$$

$$\frac{dm}{dt} = (4\pi r^2 \rho)\frac{dr}{dt}$$

The rate of increase of m is proportional to the surface area. Therefore

$$\frac{dm}{dt} = k \times 4\pi r^2$$

for some constant k. Hence

$$4\pi r^2 k = \left(4\pi r^2 \rho\right)\frac{dr}{dt}.$$

$\Rightarrow$ $$\frac{dr}{dt} = \frac{k}{\rho} = c$$

where c is a constant.

Integrating gives

$$r = ct + a$$

where the constant of integration is a, since $r = a$ when $t = 0$.

Therefore r increases linearly with t.

(iii) $$\frac{d}{dt}(mv) = mg = \frac{4}{3}\pi\rho g r^3 = \frac{4}{3}\pi\rho g (ct+a)^3$$

Integrating gives

$$mv = \frac{4\pi\rho g}{3}(ct+a)^4 \times \frac{1}{4c} + d \qquad (d \text{ is the constant of integration})$$

$$= \left(\frac{\pi\rho g}{3c}\right)r^4 + d \qquad (r = ct+a)$$

When $t = 0$, $r = a$ and $v = 0$ giving $d = -\left(\frac{\pi\rho g}{3c}\right)a^4$.

Hence

$$mv = \frac{\pi\rho g}{3c}(r^4 - a^4)$$

But $m = \frac{4}{3}\pi r^3 \rho$, thus

$$\frac{4\pi r^3 \rho v}{3} = \frac{\pi\rho g}{3c}(r^4 - a^4)$$

$\Rightarrow$ $$v = \frac{g}{4c}\left(r - \frac{a^4}{r^3}\right).$$

(iv) Acceleration $\dfrac{dv}{dt} = \dfrac{dv}{dr} \times \dfrac{dr}{dt}$

$$-\frac{g}{4c}\left(1 + \frac{3a^4}{r^4}\right)\frac{dr}{dt}$$

$$= \frac{g}{4} + \frac{3g}{4}\left(\frac{a}{r}\right)^4 \quad \text{since} \frac{dr}{dt} = c$$

when $r = a, \dfrac{dv}{dt} = g$ as expected (initial acceleration).

When $r \gg a$, the second term is negligible, thus the acceleration is

approximately $\dfrac{g}{4}$.

EXERCISE 2A

1 The following three situations are all different. Use a momentum–impulse equation over a short time δt as in Examples 2.1 and 2.2 to obtain the equation of motion for each object.

   (i) A snowball grows as it rolls unaided across horizontal ground.

   (ii) A hailstone grows as it falls through a cloud of ice crystals.

   (iii) A forward driving force, F, acts on a truck which is dropping gravel along a footpath.

2 A charged droplet of mass M, initially at rest, is under the influence of a constant horizontal electrical force of magnitude F. The droplet evaporates so that at time t its mass is Me^{-kt}, where k is a positive constant.

   (i) Show that the equation of motion in the direction of the electrical force is

$$F = Me^{-kt}\frac{dv}{dt}$$

   where v is the speed of the droplet in this direction.

   (ii) Solve this equation to express v in terms of t.

3 A wagon containing sand moves under a constant horizontal force F while the sand drops out at a constant rate k. The wagon is initially at rest with a total mass M of which the mass of sand is m_0.

   What velocity does it have when all the sand has gone?

4 As it moves forward, a dumper truck is releasing topsoil at a rate of r kg s^{-1}. The net forward force on the truck works at a constant rate of P kW. Initially the truck is at rest and the total load (truck plus soil) is M_0 kg. The soil drops out of the truck with no horizontal velocity relative to the truck.

   (i) Show that the equation of motion may be written

$$1000P = \left(M_0 - rt\right)v\frac{dv}{dt}.$$

(ii) Solve the equation to express v^2 in terms of t.

Hence show that when the initial load is 25 tonnes, $r = 50$ and $P = 20$, the truck moves at just over $7\ ms^{-1}$ after half a minute.

5 A trailer releasing fertiliser is being pulled across a field by a constant force F. In order to give an even spread, the releasing mechanism ensures that the rate of release, $r\ kg\ s^{-1}$ is proportional to the speed of the trailer: $r = kv$, where k is constant. Fertiliser release starts when the mass of the trailer plus load is M and its speed is u.

(i) Show that the total mass of the trailer after it has moved a distance s is $M - ks$.

(ii) Write the equation of motion in terms of v and s.

(iii) Show that

$$v^2 = u^2 - \frac{2F}{K}\ln\left(1 - \frac{ks}{M}\right)$$

(iv) Confirm that as $k \to 0$, the formula becomes

$$v^2 = u^2 + \frac{2F}{M}s$$

(Use the series expansion of $\ln(1 + x)$.)

6 An oil sheikh decides to tow icebergs to the Middle East for fresh water. The iceberg is modelled as a homogeneous sphere of radius r, which melts at a rate proportional to its surface area.

(i) Show that $\dfrac{dr}{dt}$ is constant.

An iceberg has an initial mass M and one eighth of its mass remains after a time T.

(ii) Show that after time t, its mass is

$$M\left(1 - \frac{t}{2T}\right)^3.$$

(iii) Assuming a net towing force which works at a constant rate P, write down the equation of motion.

(iv) Assuming the iceberg starts from rest and has a velocity V at time T, show that

$$V^2 = \frac{6TP}{M}.$$

7 A raindrop falls vertically from rest through a mist under the influence of gravity. It grows by condensation of mist droplets, initially at rest, on its surface. After falling for a time t, the mass of the raindrop is Me^{kt}, where M and k are positive constants. After a time T the mass has increased to $2M$.

   (i) Determine the value of k in terms of T.

   (ii) Formulate the equation of motion of the raindrop.

   (iii) Show that the speed of the raindrop at time T is $\dfrac{gT}{2\ln 2}$.

   (iv) Determine how far it has fallen in time T in terms of g and T.

   [MEI]

8 A raindrop falling through stationary mist may be modelled as a uniform sphere whose radius r increases according to the law $\dfrac{dr}{dt} = kr$, where k is constant.

   Assuming the only force is gravity, show that the raindrop approaches a limiting velocity of $\dfrac{g}{3k}$.

9 The mass m of a raindrop falling under gravity through a stationary cloud increases at a constant rate k. The resistance to motion may be modelled as kv, where v is the velocity of the raindrop.

   (i) Show that the dimensions of k are consistent in the preceding two statements.

   (ii) Show that the equation of motion can be written as

   $$m\frac{dv}{dm} + 2v = \frac{mg}{k}.$$

   (iii) Show that the equation in part **(ii)** can also be written as

   $$\frac{d(m^2 v)}{dm} = \frac{m^2 g}{k}.$$

   (iv) Assuming the raindrop is initially at rest, find v in terms of g, k, m and the initial mass M.

10 A train of mass M moving under a force with constant power P picks up stationary water at a rate k. The initial velocity is v_0. Show that when the total mass (train plus water) is m, its velocity v satisfies the equation

   $$k\left(m^2 v^2 - M^2 v_0^2\right) = P\left(m^2 - M^2\right).$$

11 A spherical water droplet falls from rest through a stationary light mist. The mist condenses evenly over its surface as it falls.

(i) By considering a mass m falling with speed v coalescing with a small mass δm initially at rest, derive the equation of motion

$$\frac{d}{dt}(mv) = mg.$$

The droplet is initially of radius a and its mass increases at a rate proportional to its instantaneous surface area.

(ii) Denoting the constant of proportionality by k and the density of water by ρ show that the radius r of the droplet at time t after it starts to fall is given by

$$r = a + \frac{k}{\rho}t.$$

(iii) Find an expression for the instantaneous speed of the droplet as a function of a, g, r, k and ρ.

(iv) Hence find an expression for the instantaneous acceleration in terms of a, g and r.

(v) Deduce that the initial acceleration is g and that when r is much greater than a the acceleration tends to $\frac{g}{4}$.

[MEI]

12 An avalanche of snow slides from rest down a slope of inclination α to the horizontal. The coefficient of friction for moving snow is μ ($\mu < \tan \alpha$). The avalanche gathers snow which is initially at rest. The mass M of the avalanche at any time is given by $M = m(1 + kx)$ where m and k are constants and x is the distance moved by the avalanche down the slope.

(i) Show that the speed v of the avalanche satisfies the differential equation

$$(1 + kx)v\frac{dv}{dx} + kv^2 = (1 + kx)(\sin \alpha - \mu \cos \alpha)g.$$

(ii) Differentiate $(1 + kx)^2 v^2$ with respect to x. By comparing this result with the left-hand side of the differential equation, solve the equation to find the speed v in terms of the distance x that the avalanche has moved down the slope.

(iii) Show that when x becomes large the acceleration of the avalanche approaches a constant value.

[MEI]

13 An electron of mass m_0 is initially at rest when an electric field is applied to it. This field subjects the electron to a force of magnitude E in a constant direction. When the electron is moving very fast, its mass as measured by a stationary observer increases to

$$m = \frac{m_0}{\sqrt{1 - \left(\dfrac{v}{c}\right)^2}}$$

where the constant c is the velocity of light. (This is a consequence of Einstein's special theory of relativity.)

(i) Assuming Newton's second law applies, that force is rate of change of momentum, show that

$$v^2 = \frac{c^2 k^2 t^2}{1 + k^2 t^2} \qquad \text{where} \quad k = \frac{E}{cm_0}.$$

Deduce that the velocity of the electron never reaches the velocity of light.

(ii) Find the distance travelled by the electron after time T.

(iii) Use the binomial expansion of $(1 + x)^{-\frac{3}{2}}$ to show that when $kt \ll 1$, the distance travelled is approximately what it would have been if the mass had remained constant at m_0.

14 A particle of initial mass M falls from rest under gravity through a stationary cloud. The particle picks up mass from the cloud at a rate equal to mkv, where m and v are the mass and speed of the particle at time t and k is a constant. Resistance to motion can be neglected.

(i) Write down differential equations which describe
 (a) the increase in mass of the particle
 (b) the motion of the particle.
 Hence show that the speed satisfies the differential equation

$$v\frac{\mathrm{d}v}{\mathrm{d}x} + kv^2 = g, \qquad \text{where x is the distance fallen.}$$

(ii) By solving the equation in part **(i)** find v in terms of g, k and x.

 Deduce that the speed tends to the limiting value $\sqrt{\dfrac{g}{k}}$.

(iii) Show that $\dfrac{\mathrm{d}m}{\mathrm{d}x} = km$. Hence show that the mass of the particle is $2M$ when its speed is a fraction $\dfrac{\sqrt{3}}{2}$ of its limiting value.

[MEI]

Rockets

One of the most interesting applications of variable mass methods is the motion of rockets. The rocket stores a large amount of fuel which is burnt and ejected at very high speed and it gains forward momentum to compensate for the backward momentum of the expelled fuel. Rockets are normally designed so that the fuel leaves the rocket at a constant mass rate and at a constant velocity *relative to the rocket*. This is more complicated than Example 2.2, where the lost mass simply had the *same* velocity as the truck.

The motion of a rocket

You can analyse rocket motion by working from first principles as before. In this case assume that fuel is ejected at a constant speed of u relative to the rocket so its speed in the direction of motion is $v - u$. Again the mass, m, of the rocket is decreasing and this means that δm is negative, so use $|\delta m|$ for the mass ejected over time δt. Figure 2.6 summarises the situation.

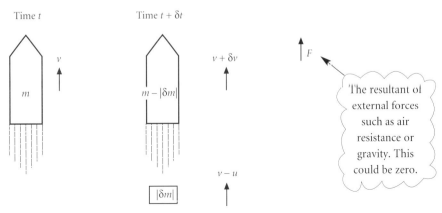

Time t

Time $t + \delta t$

v

m

$v + \delta v$

$m - |\delta m|$

$v - u$

$|\delta m|$

F

The resultant of external forces such as air resistance or gravity. This could be zero.

Figure 2.6

The gain in momentum is equal to the impulse of the force so

$$(m-|\delta m|)(v+\delta v)+|\delta m|(v-u)-mv = F\delta t$$

$$\Rightarrow \quad m\delta v-|\delta m|\delta v-|\delta m|u = F\delta t$$

$$\Rightarrow \quad m\frac{\delta v}{\delta t}-\frac{|\delta m|}{\delta t}\delta v-\frac{|\delta m|}{\delta t}u = F.$$

> As before, any small variation in F over the time δt disappears, so the force, F, does not have to be constant.

In the limit as $\delta t \to 0$, this gives

$$m\frac{dv}{dt}-\left|\frac{dm}{dt}\right|u = F$$

$$m\frac{dv}{dt}= F+\left|\frac{dm}{dt}\right|u.$$

There is a forward thrust, $\left|\dfrac{dm}{dt}\right|u$, caused by the ejection of the fuel.

Notice that the force, F, is assumed to be in the direction of motion of the rocket, so it is *negative* when the rocket is leaving the Earth's surface.

In the following example $\left|\dfrac{dm}{dt}\right|$ is replaced by the rate, k, at which the fuel is burnt. This example demonstrates the essential mathematical principles of rocket motion.

EXAMPLE 2.4

At time t, a rocket in one-dimensional motion has mass m, is travelling with speed v and is burning fuel at a constant mass rate k. The burnt fuel is ejected with a constant exhaust speed u relative to the rocket. Such a rocket has initial mass m_0, of which a fraction α is fuel, and is fired vertically upwards from rest in a constant gravitational field g.

(i) By considering the momentum over a small period, derive the equation of motion

$$(m_0-kt)\frac{dv}{dt}=ku-(m_0-kt)g.$$

(ii) Write down a condition for the rocket to start rising when its motor is fired.

(iii) For how long will the motor burn?

(iv) Assuming that the rocket does start to rise immediately, find its final speed when all the fuel has burnt.

(v) Use the expression derived in part (iv) to suggest ways in which the final speed might be increased, assuming that the initial mass m_0 is fixed.

[MEI]

SOLUTION

(i) At time t, the mass of the rocket is $m = m_0 - kt$ and the momentum is mv.

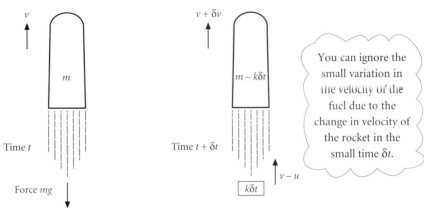

Figure 2.7

At a small time δt later, an amount of mass $k\delta t$ has been expelled at a speed of u relative to the rocket. The velocity of the fuel is thus $(v - u)$ upwards. At time $t + \delta t$, the velocity of the rocket has increased to $v + \delta v$. The momentum at time $t + \delta t$ is

$$(m - k\delta t)(v + \delta v) + k\delta t (v - u) = mv + m\delta v - k\delta t u - k\delta t \delta v$$

The *increase* in momentum over this period is thus approximately $m\delta v - k\delta t u - k\delta t \delta v$.

This is equal to the impulse of the external force which is $-mg\delta t$.

$$-mg\delta t = m\delta v - k\delta t u - k\delta t \delta v$$

$$\Rightarrow \qquad -mg = m\frac{\delta v}{\delta t} - ku - ku\delta v$$

As $\delta t \to 0, \dfrac{\delta v}{\delta t} \to \dfrac{dv}{dt}$. The term $-ku\delta v$ tends to zero, so

You can ignore the small variation in the velocity of the fuel due to the change in velocity of the rocket in the small time δt.

$$-mg = m\frac{dv}{dt} - ku$$

$$\Rightarrow \qquad m\frac{dv}{dt} = ku - mg$$

Compare with $ma = F$. The left-hand side is mass × acceleration of the rocket. The right-hand side, in addition to the external force of gravity, includes a term ku which can be interpreted as the forward force (thrust) of the engine; it is the *rate of change of momentum of the expelled mass*.

Substituting $m = m_0 - kt$, gives the required result.

$$(m_0 - kt)\frac{dv}{dt} = ku - (m_0 - kt)g$$

(ii) $$(m_0 - kt)\frac{dv}{dt} = ku - (m_0 - kt)g$$

When the rocket is fired, $t = 0$. For the rocket to start rising, the acceleration must be positive, i.e. $\frac{dv}{dt} > 0$. Hence

$$ku - m_0 g > 0$$

$$\Rightarrow \quad ku > m_0 g.$$

The thrust of the engine, ku, must be greater than the gravitational force $m_0 g$.

(iii) The motor burns as long as there is fuel. Since the total fuel is αm_0, then when all the fuel is burnt

$$\alpha m_0 = kt \quad \Rightarrow \quad t = \frac{\alpha m_0}{k}.$$

(iv) From part **(i)**

$$\frac{dv}{dt} = \frac{ku}{m_0 - kt} - g.$$

Integrating gives

$$v = -u\ln(m_0 - kt) - gt + c \qquad ①$$

where c is the constant of integration. When $t = 0$, $v = 0$, so $c = u\ln m_0$.

Substituting $t = \frac{\alpha m_0}{k}$ gives the final velocity

$$v_f = u\ln\left(\frac{m_0}{m_0 - \alpha m_0}\right) - \frac{g\alpha m_0}{k}$$

$$= u\ln\left(\frac{1}{1-\alpha}\right) - \frac{g\alpha m_0}{k}. \qquad ②$$

(v) An increase in v_f can be achieved by increasing the first term or decreasing the second. The possibilities are

- increase u: use a fuel with a high exhaust rate
- make α near 1: increase the proportion of the total mass that is fuel
- make k larger: increase the burn rate.

Rocket motion with no external force

If the rocket is fired in space where there is no appreciable external force, the rocket equation is simply

$$m\frac{dv}{dt} = ku$$

where, using the notation of Example 2.4, u is the relative exhaust speed, m is the rocket mass at a given time and $k = -\dfrac{dm}{dt}$ is the rate at which fuel is burned.

The effective thrust of the engine is:

(rate of expulsion of mass, relative to the rocket) × (relative speed of the fuel).

Equation ② from Example 2.4 is

$$v_f = u \ln\left(\frac{1}{1 - \alpha}\right)$$

Replace g by zero.

or

$$v_f = u \ln\left(\frac{m_0}{m_0 - \alpha m_0}\right)$$

$$= u \ln\left(\frac{\text{initial mass}}{\text{final mass}}\right).$$

The final velocity depends only on u, the relative velocity of the fuel, and on the proportion of the total mass that is fuel. Note that k does not appear in this expression. When there is no external force, the rate at which mass is burned does not affect the *final* velocity, although it obviously determines how long the rocket takes to reach this velocity.

If the rocket begins with some initial velocity v_0, ① gives $c = v_0 + u \ln m_0$. Then the result is

$$v_f - v_0 = u \ln\left(\frac{\text{initial mass}}{\text{final mass}}\right).$$

$(v_f - v_0)$ is the *velocity gained* over the burn period.

EXAMPLE 2.5

A spaceship is pointing towards a planet. The initial total mass of the ship is M_0 kg and the fuel is ejected at a rate of k kg s⁻¹ with a speed u ms⁻¹ relative to the spaceship. The ship starts at rest relative to the planet, and its speed, when all the fuel is exhausted, is $2u$ ms⁻¹. However, it is still so far from the planet that the gravitational force can be neglected.

(i) From the equation of motion derive an expression for v in terms of the remaining mass m at any time.

Hence show that the total mass at the end is $\dfrac{M_0}{e^2}$ kg.

(ii) Find the velocity of the *ejected fuel* relative to the planet just before the end of the period. Comment on this result.

(iii) Show that the distance travelled during the period of the rocket firing is

$$\frac{M_0 u}{k e^2}(e^2 - 3).$$

SOLUTION

(i) After time t, the mass of the ship is $m = M_0 - kt$. Since there are no external forces, the equation of motion is

$$m\frac{dv}{dt} = ku$$

$$\frac{dv}{dt} = \frac{ku}{(M_0 - kt)}.$$

Integrating gives

$$v = -u\ln(M_0 - kt) + c.$$

When $t = 0$, $v = 0$, so $c = u\ln(M_0)$. This gives

$$v = u\ln\left(\frac{M_0}{M_0 - kt}\right) = u\ln\left(\frac{M_0}{m}\right) \qquad \textcircled{1}$$

At the end of the burn, $v = 2u$, giving

$$\ln\left(\frac{M_0}{m}\right) = 2$$

$$\frac{M_0}{m} = e^2$$

$$\Rightarrow \qquad m = \frac{M_0}{e^2}$$

(ii) At the end of the burn period, the velocity of the fuel relative to the planet is $2u - u = u$ ms^{-1}. The expelled fuel is actually travelling *towards* the planet, although not as fast as the rocket! There is no paradox here; all velocities are relative.

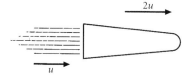

Figure 2.8

(iii) From $\textcircled{1}$

$$\frac{ds}{dt} = u\ln\left(\frac{M_0}{M_0 - kt}\right)$$

where s is the displacement from the start. Integrating gives

$$s = u\int\ln\left(\frac{M_0}{M_0 - kt}\right)dt$$

$$= u \int \ln M_0 \, dt - u \int \ln(M_0 - kt) \, dt.$$ ②

The second integral is easier if you make the substitution $m = M_0 - kt$.

$$\int \ln(M_0 - kt) \, dt = -\frac{1}{k} \int \ln m \, dm$$

$$= -\frac{1}{k}(m \ln m - m) + \text{constant}$$

You can use integration by parts with $u = \ln x$, $\frac{du}{dx} = 1$ to show that $\int \ln x \, dx = x \ln x - x.$

Substituting this in ② gives

$$s = ut \ln M_0 + \frac{mu}{k}(\ln m - 1) + c$$

When $s = 0$, $t = 0$, $m = M_0$. So

$$c = -\frac{M_0 u}{k}(\ln M_0 - 1)$$

Hence

$$s = ut \ln M_0 + \frac{mu}{k}(\ln m - 1) - \frac{M_0 u}{k}(\ln M_0 - 1)$$ ③

At burn out, $m = \dfrac{M_0}{e^2}$ (proved in part **(i)**)

$$\Rightarrow \quad M_0 - kT = \frac{M_0}{e^2}$$

where T is time of burn out

$$\Rightarrow \quad T = \frac{M_0}{ke^2}(e^2 - 1)$$

Substituting $m = \dfrac{M_0}{e^2}$ and $t = T = \dfrac{M_0}{ke^2}(e^2 - 1)$ in ③ gives

$$s = \frac{uM_0}{ke^2}(e^2 - 1)\ln M_0 + \frac{M_0 u}{ke^2}\left(\ln\left(\frac{M_0}{e^2}\right) - 1\right) - \frac{M_0 u}{k}(\ln M_0 - 1)$$

$$= \frac{M_0 u}{ke^2}\left[(e^2 \ln M_0 - \ln M_0) + (\ln M_0 - 2 - 1) - (e^2 \ln M_0 - e^2)\right]$$

$$= \frac{M_0 u}{ke^2}(e^2 - 3)$$

$\ln e^2 = 2$

Historical note

The first rockets were probably bamboo tubes packed with 'black powder', a precursor of gunpowder. These were used by the Chinese in the 10th century. The technology spread both for warfare and entertainment; from the 16th century onwards, firework displays with rockets were used widely in Europe. Rockets were successfully used against the British by Indian forces during the battles of Seringapatam in 1792 and 1799. As a result, the British army adopted rockets for military purposes and used them for most of the next century. A typical military rocket of that time was described as an iron cylinder, 200 mm long, 40 mm wide with a 3 m guiding stick. By the end of the 19th century, better artillery superseded the rocket and the military lost interest. A few enthusiasts maintained development in rocket technology during the following decades until World War 2 when Germany developed the V2. This could reach a target some 300 km away in 5 minutes. Despite many technical problems, it was used to devastating effect, with about 1500 landing in southern England. With the end of the war, and the beginning of the Cold War, most work on the development of rockets moved to the USA and USSR.

In 1957, the space age began, with the USSR putting the first artificial satellite, Sputnik, into orbit. This led to manned space launches, the most spectacular of which was the moon landing in 1969. Huge rockets were built: the first stage of the enormous Saturn V rocket which put the first men on the moon had a thrust of 3.4×10^7 N.

The huge growth in the need for satellites for communication purposes has meant that rocket technology has continued to develop and the space rocket is now a standard part of contemporary technology.

Jet aircraft

Figure 2.9

A jet aircraft is propelled in a similar way to a rocket, in the sense that propulsion is achieved by expelling mass. However, the engine uses the surrounding medium in that it takes in air at the front, compresses it and ejects it at high speed (see figure 2.9). The only change in mass is the expenditure of some fuel also expelled as exhaust gases, but this is small compared with the mass of air. Assuming air is entering and leaving at a mass rate k, the aircraft is moving at a velocity v relative to the air, and expels it at a rate u relative to the aircraft, the effective thrust is the rate of change of momentum of this air, which is $k(u - v)$.

Unlike a rocket, it is impossible for the aircraft, in still air, to achieve a speed greater than the relative speed of ejection of the fuel.

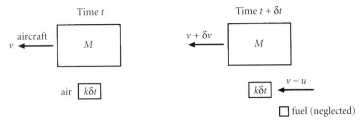

Figure 2.10

A mass of still air $k\delta t$ is picked up and expelled in a time period δt. Equating linear momentum before and after this period (see figure 2.10):

$$Mv + k\delta t \times 0 = M(v + \delta v) - k\delta t(u - v)$$
$$M\delta v = k\delta t(u - v)$$
$$M\frac{\delta v}{\delta t} = k(u - v)$$

In the limit, the effective thrust $M\dfrac{dv}{dt}$ is $k(u - v)$.

INVESTIGATIONS

Multistage rockets

This investigation uses the result on page 63 which gives the gain in velocity of a rocket when gravitational forces are ignored and there are no external forces, as

$$v_f - v_0 = u\ln\left(\frac{\text{initial mass}}{\text{final mass}}\right)$$

The increase in velocity is proportional to u, the exhaust speed of the fuel, so fuels are chosen which would burn with a high exhaust speed.

Note also that the larger the proportion of the initial mass which is fuel, the greater will be the gain in velocity. However, there is a limit here. The rocket is being used to move some payload – whether a communications satellite or three astronauts and their dog – and that is not part of the fuel. Also the fuel must be contained in some casing. If the amount of fuel is increased, the size and therefore the mass of this casing is increased.

Suppose the payload mass is m kg and the total mass (rocket plus payload) is Nm kg. Therefore, the fuel plus casing has a mass $(N - 1)m$ kg. Assume that only a fraction α of this is fuel.

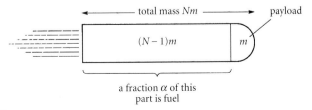

Figure 2.11

(i)   Given a fuel ejection velocity of u km s^{-1}, what gain in velocity is achieved by the rocket?

(ii)   The velocity gain can be increased by building a bigger rocket: increasing N. But assuming α is constant, there is an upper limit to what can be achieved. What is the limit?

(iii) Taking $u = 2000$ and $\alpha = 0.9$, plot the gain in velocity against N.

Two-stage rockets

The way round this limit is to use multistage rockets. A sequence of rockets is used and once one has burned all its fuel, its casing separates from the rest.

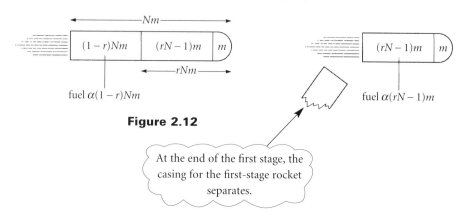

Figure 2.12

At the end of the first stage, the casing for the first-stage rocket separates.

Suppose the whole system has a *total mass Nm*, but is divided into two stages (as in figure 2.12). The second stage carries the payload and has a total mass of rNm, where $0 < r < 1$. The first stage, simply a rocket with fuel and casing has mass $(1 - r)Nm$ and so contains $\alpha(1 - r)Nm$ fuel. In the first part of the trip, stage 1 fuel is all burnt, giving a gain in velocity, v_1. The casing from stage 1 is then jettisoned. This leaves the second stage and the payload: there is a mass of fuel, $\alpha(rN - 1)m$. This is then burned, giving another gain in velocity, v_2.

 For some value of N investigate graphically how the total gain in velocity varies for different values of r and hence find when the gain is a maximum. Use the values of α and u from part **(iii)** above. If you do this for different values of N, you should spot a relationship between r and N when the gain is a maximum. There is also a simple relationship between v_1 and v_2 for maximum gain. You could obtain these theoretically by differentiation assuming N is constant.

Practical rocket experiments

Some model shops sell rockets where burning rates and thrusts are supplied (for examples, see Question 2 in Exercise 2B). Devise simple experiments you could do with such rockets which would enable you to verify the principles of rocket motion given in this chapter.

1 A balloon is blown up and let go so that it shoots away in a horizontal direction. Assuming that air is expelled at a constant speed, c, relative to the balloon and that the mass of air in the balloon decreases at a constant rate, k, use a momentum–impulse equation over a short time δt to obtain the equation of motion of the balloon.

There is an increase in kinetic energy when the balloon is released. Where does this energy come from?

2 A rocket expels fuel at a constant relative velocity u. The mass of the rocket at time t is m and the fuel is used at a constant rate k, so that $\dfrac{dm}{dt} = -k$.

(i) Assuming no external forces act on the rocket, use conservation of linear momentum to show that

$$m\frac{dv}{dt} = ku$$

where v is the velocity of the rocket at time t.

(ii) The following data have been published for a range of model rockets.

Model	Time of burn	Thrust	Mass of fuel
R1	0.216 s	5.80 N	2.03 g
R2	0.325 s	7.70 N	4.16 g
R3	1.20 s	4.15 N	8.33 g
R4	0.862 s	5.80 N	6.23 g
R5	0.625 s	8.00 N	6.23 g
R6	1.72 s	5.80 N	12.5 g
R7	1.70 s	11.80 N	24.9 g

Work out the relative expulsion speed of the fuel (ms^{-1}) in each case. How many distinct fuels do you think are used in this range of rockets?

3 A rocket expels fuel at a constant relative velocity u. The mass of the rocket at time t is m and the fuel is used at a constant rate k.

(i) Show that the motion of a rocket launched upwards under gravity is governed by the equation

$$m\frac{dv}{dt} = ku - mg$$

and hence prove that the velocity after time t is given by

$$v = u\ln\left(\frac{m_0}{m_0 - kt}\right) - gt$$

where m_0 is the initial total mass.

(ii) A model rocket, R5, has the following characteristics.

Time of burn:	0.625s
Thrust:	8.00 N
Mass of fuel	6.23 g

Assume that the mass of fuel represents 80% of the total rocket mass. What will be the velocity of R5 at burnout if it is launched upwards from rest?

4 A rocket of initial total mass M burns fuel at a constant rate rM and expels the fuel with a constant relative velocity u. When the rocket is launched vertically under gravity, the thrust is just sufficient for the rocket to rise.

(i) Show that $ru = g$.

(ii) Show that when a mass M' remains, the rocket's velocity is

$$u\ln\left(\frac{M}{M'}\right) - u\left(1 - \frac{M'}{M}\right).$$

5 A rocket under no external forces has a mass m and velocity v at time t and expels fuel backwards at a mass rate k and a relative speed u.

(i) Write down the equation of motion.

(ii) By considering the change in *total* kinetic energy (rocket and expelled fuel) over a small interval δt, show that the rate of gain of total kinetic energy is $\frac{1}{2}ku^2$.

6 A rocket-propelled vehicle starts from rest with mass M and ejects fuel at a constant mass rate r per unit time with a constant relative speed u. When travelling horizontally with speed v the total resistance to motion is kv.

(i) Show that its acceleration at time t is $\dfrac{ru - kv}{m}$ where $m = M - rt$.

(ii) Show that its speed at time t is $\dfrac{ru}{k}\left[1 - \left(\dfrac{m}{M}\right)^{k/r}\right]$.

7 At time t a rocket in one-dimensional motion has mass M, is travelling with speed v and is burning fuel at a constant mass rate k. The burnt fuel is ejected with a constant exhaust speed c relative to the rocket. The rocket has an initial mass of M_0, of which a fraction α is fuel, and is fired from rest in a gravity-free environment.

(i) Write down the mass of the rocket after time t and find the time for which the fuel burns.

(ii) Derive the equation of motion

$$M\frac{\mathrm{d}v}{\mathrm{d}t} = kc.$$

The mass ratio R of a rocket is defined to be the mass of the rocket when fuelled divided by the mass when empty.

(iii) Show that the final speed, V, of the rocket is given by

$$V = -c\ln(1-\alpha) = c\ln R.$$

A two-stage rocket consists of a first stage of mass M_1 which carries a second stage of mass M_2. Each stage has a fraction α of fuel and $M_1 + M_2 = M_0$. The first stage is fired from rest and carries the second stage until all of the first-stage fuel is burnt. At this point the second stage separates and its motor is fired until all of its fuel is burnt.

(iv) Find the mass ratios R_1 and R_2 of the first stage (carrying the second) and the second stage of the rocket.

(v) Determine the speed of the two-stage system at separation in terms of c and R_1.

(vi) Find the final speed of the second stage in terms of c, R_1 and R_2.

[MEI]

8 At time t a rocket has a mass m and is in one-dimensional motion with speed v. The exhaust of burnt fuel is expelled with a constant speed c relative to the rocket. Derive the differential equation

$$m\frac{\mathrm{d}v}{\mathrm{d}t} + c\frac{\mathrm{d}m}{\mathrm{d}t} = F$$

where F is the total external force.

A rocket initially of mass M, of which a fraction α is fuel, $0 < \alpha < 1$, burns fuel at a constant mass rate k. The burnt fuel is expelled with constant exhaust speed c relative to the rocket. The rocket is fired vertically upwards in a constant gravitational field g. Air resistance is neglected. If the rocket starts to rise immediately upon ignition, find its speed and altitude when all the fuel has burnt.

(The result $\int \ln x \,\mathrm{d}x = x(\ln x - 1) + C$ may be assumed.)

[MEI]

9 An amateur designer creates a small rocket which burns fuel so that the rocket loses mass at the constant rate k. The initial total mass of the rocket and fuel is M_0 and the initial mass of fuel is $\frac{1}{2}M_0$.

(i) Write down an expression for the mass m of the rocket and remaining fuel at any later time t, while the fuel is still burning.

The burnt fuel is expelled from the rocket with a constant speed c (backwards) relative to the rocket. The rocket is fired vertically upwards and air resistance may be neglected. At time $t = 0$, the rocket lifts from the ground. After a time t, the speed of the rocket is denoted by v.

(ii) Show that the differential equation describing the motion of the rocket is

$$m\frac{dv}{dt} = kc - mg, \quad \text{provided that } M_0g < kc.$$

Why is this inequality necessary?

(iii) Show that the speed of the rocket while the fuel is still burning is given by

$$v = c\ln\left(\frac{M_0}{M_0 - kt}\right) - gt.$$

(iv) Find the greatest speed of the rocket while it is still moving upwards.

[MEI]

10 At time t, a rocket moving in free space has total mass m and speed v. Fuel is burnt at a constant mass rate k and is ejected with speed c relative to the rocket. The initial total mass of the rocket is M, of which a mass αM is fuel. At time $t = 0$ the rocket is at rest.

(i) Find an expression for m in terms of M, k and t.
Find also the time for which the fuel burns.

(ii) Show that the equation of motion for the rocket can be written $m\dfrac{dv}{dt} = kc$.

(iii) By solving the equation in part **(ii)**, show that

$$v = c\ln\left(\frac{M}{m}\right).$$

Hence find the final speed, V, of the rocket.

In an early test flight of the rocket, a fault in the control system meant that the first 25% of the total mass of fuel was ejected at speed $\frac{1}{2}c$ relative to the rocket although the fuel was burnt at the correct rate. The remainder of the fuel was burnt at the correct rate and ejected at speed c relative to the rocket.

(iv) Show that the final speed, W, that was achieved in that case is given by

$$W = \frac{1}{2}c\ln\left(\frac{1 - \frac{1}{4}\alpha}{(1-\alpha)^2}\right).$$

[MEI]

In the following, F is the external force on a body whose mass is changing, m is the mass of the body at time t, and v is its velocity.

The first key point is the crucial one, from which the others follow.

1 The standard approach to variable mass problems is to apply the principle

    change in momentum = impulse of force

over a small time interval t to $t + \delta t$. The change in the force over this interval may be neglected.

2 Newton's second law can be used directly in the form

    external force = rate of change of *total* momentum.

However, you must ensure that this takes into account the *total* momentum change in the system.

3 For a body losing mass, where the lost mass maintains its momentum as it leaves, (e.g. coal dropping from a hopper truck), the equation becomes

$$F = m\frac{dv}{dt}.$$

4 For a body gaining mass, where the extra mass previously has no velocity (e.g. moisture from still air condensing on to a raindrop), the equation is

$$F = \frac{d}{dt}(mv) = m\frac{dv}{dt} + v\frac{dm}{dt}.$$

5 For a rocket expelling mass at a constant rate k with a relative velocity u opposite to the direction of rocket motion

$$m\frac{dv}{dt} = ku + F$$

where ku may be regarded as the thrust on the rocket due to the burning of fuel.

6 A rocket under no external force will have a velocity gain given by

$$v_f - v_0 = u\ln\left(\frac{\text{initial mass}}{\text{final mass}}\right).$$

The moment of inertia of a rotating body

The human mind has first to construct forms, independently, before we can find them in things.

Einstein, 1879–1955

❓ So far you have modelled moving objects as particles. In many circumstances this is reasonable, but how would you model the motion of the sails of a windmill or the other objects illustrated in the pictures above?

Do the two children on the roundabout have the same kinetic energy?

What is the kinetic energy of a rotating wheel?

A rigid body rotating about a fixed axis

You might not be able to answer all these questions fully now, but the issues involved should become clearer as you work through this chapter.

It is reasonable to treat a large object as a particle when every part of it is moving in the same direction with the same speed, but clearly this is not always the case. The particles in a rotating wheel have different velocities and accelerations and are subject to different forces.

The laws of particle dynamics which you have used so far need to be developed so that they can be applied to the rotation of large objects.

Definitions

You are already familiar with many aspects of rotation such as the angular speed and acceleration of a particle and you have also taken moments to determine the turning effect of a force, but it is as well to be clear about what is meant by some of the terms involved before continuing with the discussion.

Rigid bodies

Wheels can be modelled as rigid bodies. A *rigid body* is such that each point within it is always the same distance from any other point. You are not a rigid body but a hard chair is one (molecular vibrations being ignored).

The axis of rotation

When you lean back on your chair, it might rotate about a point, say A, at the end of one leg. You will have more control, however, if it rotates about the axis formed by the line joining the ends, A and B, of two legs.

The idea of an axis of rotation is important when considering the rotation of rigid bodies. When the only fixed point is A, the axis of rotation might be continually changing, any particle in the chair moves on the surface of a sphere with its centre at A. When the chair rotates about the *fixed axis* AB, however, each particle in it moves in a circle in a plane perpendicular to the axis (see figure 3.1). The problems you meet in *Mechanics 4* will always have a fixed axis of rotation.

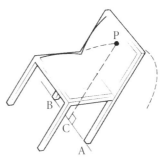

Figure 3.1

Angular speed

You studied circular motion in *Mechanics 3*. In figure 3.2, P is moving in a circle, centre O, with an angular speed $\frac{d\theta}{dt}$ or $\dot{\theta}$ (often denoted by ω). It was shown that the speed of P is given by

$$v = r\omega.$$

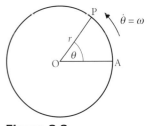

Figure 3.2

In a rigid body rotating about a fixed axis, *all* the particles have the same angular speed, ω, about the axis and the speed of each particle is given by its angular velocity times its perpendicular distance from that axis. Thus if the chair in figure 3.3 is rotating about the axis through the base of the back legs, the speed of the point P_1 is

$$v = AP_1 \times \dot{\theta}.$$

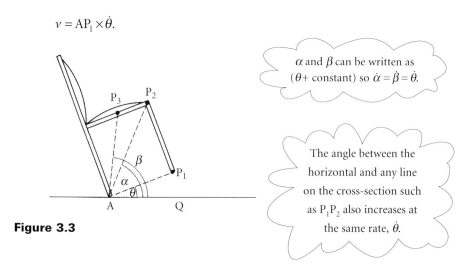

> α and β can be written as $(\theta + \text{constant})$ so $\dot{\alpha} = \dot{\beta} = \dot{\theta}$.

> The angle between the horizontal and any line on the cross-section such as P_1P_2 also increases at the same rate, $\dot{\theta}$.

Figure 3.3

The kinetic energy of a rigid body rotating about a fixed axis

Because kinetic energy is a scalar quantity, the kinetic energy of a rigid body, such as a wheel, can be found by calculating the energy of each of the separate particles and then adding them. For example, you could find the kinetic energy of the children on the roundabout by treating each one as a separate particle moving in a circle. They could be modelled as a simple rigid body like that in the next example.

EXAMPLE 3.1

A rigid body consists of two particles P_1 and P_2 of masses m_1 and m_2 attached to a light rod AB as shown in figure 3.4. $AP_1 = r_1$ and $AP_2 = r_2$ and P_2 is at B.

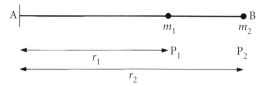

Figure 3.4

Find the kinetic energy of the body when it rotates with angular speed ω about an axis perpendicular to the rod

(i) through A

(ii) through B.

SOLUTION

(i) When the rod rotates with angular speed ω about an axis through A perpendicular to the rod, each particle moves in a circle, centre A. P_1 has speed $v_1 = r_1\omega$ and P_2 has speed $v_2 = r_2\omega$. The total kinetic energy is, therefore,

$$\tfrac{1}{2}m_1v_1^2 + \tfrac{1}{2}m_2v_2^2 = \tfrac{1}{2}m_1r_1^2\omega^2 + \tfrac{1}{2}m_2r_2^2\omega^2$$
$$= \tfrac{1}{2}(m_1r_1^2 + m_2r_2^2)\omega^2.$$

(ii) When the axis is through the end B, the particle P_2 at B does not move so has no kinetic energy. The particle P_1 now moves in a circle of radius $(r_2 - r_1)$, so the total kinetic energy is now $\tfrac{1}{2}m_1(r_2 - r_1)^2\omega^2$.

You can see that the kinetic energy depends not only on the mass of the body and the angular speed, but also on the distance of the particles of the body from the axis of rotation.

Now consider a more complex rigid body rotating with an angular speed $\dot{\theta}$. Think of it as being made up of a lot of small particles of mass, m_1, m_2, ...

A typical particle of mass m_p, moving in its circle of radius r_p round the axis of rotation with angular speed $\dot{\theta}$, has a speed $r_p\dot{\theta}$ (see figure 3.5). Its kinetic energy is $\tfrac{1}{2}m_pr_p^2\dot{\theta}^2$.

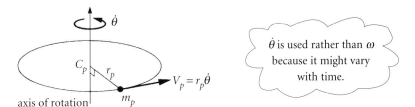

$\dot{\theta}$ is used rather than ω because it might vary with time.

Figure 3.5

Summing over all particles gives the total kinetic energy as

$$\sum_{\text{all } p}\tfrac{1}{2}m_pr_p^2\dot{\theta}^2 = \tfrac{1}{2}\left(\sum_{\text{all } p}m_pr_p^2\right)\dot{\theta}^2 \quad \text{(since } \dot{\theta} \text{ is the same for all particles).}$$

Moment of inertia

The quantity $\displaystyle\sum_{\text{all } p}m_pr_p^2$ is called the *moment of inertia* of the body about the axis and is conventionally denoted by the letter I. Moment of inertia has dimensions ML^2 and so its SI unit is $1\,\text{kg}\,\text{m}^2$.

The moment of inertia (I or $\sum m_pr_p^2$) of a body about an axis is a scalar quantity which depends on the manner in which the particles of the body are distributed about that particular axis. Its value varies according to the position and orientation of the axis.

Once you know the moment of inertia of a body about a given axis, you can find its kinetic energy when rotating about that axis. It is $\frac{1}{2}I\dot\theta^2$. Notice that there is an analogy between this expression for kinetic energy and the kinetic energy, $\frac{1}{2}mv^2$, of a particle. The mass, m, can be replaced by I and the speed, v, by the angular speed $\dot\theta$ (or ω) to give $\frac{1}{2}I\dot\theta^2$ (or $\frac{1}{2}I\omega^2$). You will see later that there are similar analogies between other quantities you have used for the motion of particles and those which apply to the rotation of a rigid body.

Inertia is a word which is used to describe a resistance to change in motion; it is sometimes used in place of mass. The larger the mass, or inertia, of a particle the greater the amount of energy required to change its motion. In the same way, the energy required to change *rotational* motion is greater for bodies with large moments of inertia.

EXAMPLE 3.2

A wooden top has a moment of inertia of 2.4×10^{-5} kg m^2 about its axis. It starts spinning when a string wound round the spindle of the top is pulled with a constant force of 0.5 N. Assuming there is no loss of energy due to friction, find the angular speed attained by the top when the length of the string is 0.3 m.

SOLUTION

The work done in pulling the string is $0.5 \times 0.3 = 0.15$ J and, as no energy is lost in the process, this is equal to the gain in kinetic energy of the top. So the angular speed attained is ω rad s^{-1}, where

$$\tfrac{1}{2} \times 2.4 \times 10^{-5}\omega^2 = 0.15$$

$$\Rightarrow \qquad \omega^2 = 12\,500$$

The angular speed is 112 rad s^{-1} correct to 3 significant figures.

The kinetic energy of a rotating wheel

So what is the kinetic energy of a rotating wheel?

As usual when modelling mechanical systems, it is useful to begin with a simple case. The simplest model of a wheel is one in which the mass of the spokes or their equivalent is negligible and all the mass can be considered to be concentrated at the rim in a hoop or ring of radius r. Then every particle is the same distance, r, from the axle. The moment of inertia of the wheel about the axle is then

$$I = \sum m_p r_p^2$$
$$= \left(\sum m_p\right) r^2$$
$$= Mr^2$$

where M is the total mass.

When this wheel is rotating with angular speed $\dot{\theta}$ about an axis through its centre perpendicular to its plane, its kinetic energy is

$$\tfrac{1}{2}I\dot{\theta}^2 = \tfrac{1}{2}Mr^2\dot{\theta}^2$$

The kinetic energy of a more complex wheel can be found when you know its moment of inertia, I, about the axis of rotation.

Radius of gyration

The moment of inertia, I, of a body about a given axis of rotation depends on the mass of the body, M, and its distribution around that axis – as you have seen, parts of the body further away from the axis contribute more. The *radius of gyration* of the body about the given axis is defined as

$$k = \sqrt{\frac{I}{M}}$$

so $\qquad I = Mk^2$.

The significance of k is that if all the mass of the body were concentrated as a particle at a distance k from the axis (or in a ring of radius k) it would have the *same* moment of inertia as the original body.

❓ The T-shaped lamina can be rotated about three axes (perpendicular to its plane) in the positions shown in figure 3.6.

Which positions give the least and the greatest radius of gyration? Explain why.

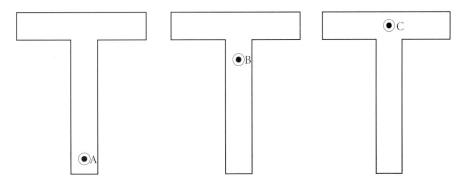

Figure 3.6

1 The diagrams show some models which have been made by joining equal light rods of length a with beads. The beads are each of mass m and can be treated as particles. Using the definition $I = \Sigma\, mr^2$, find the moments of inertia of each model about the given axes in terms of a and m, and also in terms of a and the total mass M of the model.

Model:	Axes:
(i)	$\perp$ to AB through O $\perp$ to AB through A
(ii)	AB AC $\perp$ to plane ABCD through A
(iii)	$\perp$ to BC through A AB $\perp$ to plane ABC through A $\perp$ to plane ABC through the centre of mass, G
(iv)	$\perp$ to BCDE through A DC

2 (i) Use the formula $\frac{1}{2}Mr^2$ (proved in Example 3.3) to calculate the moment of inertia about its axis of a flywheel which is a uniform disc of mass 10 kg and radius 0.25 m.

(ii) Find the kinetic energy required to change its angular speed from 50 to 100 rad s^{-1}.

3 A drum majorette twirls a baton of mass 0.4 kg and length 0.7 m in a circle around its centre. She says that the end moves at speeds up to 30 mph. Assuming the baton is a thin rod, use the formula $\frac{1}{3}Ml^2$ (see page 85) to calculate its moment of inertia and find its kinetic energy in this case. (Note 1 mile $\approx$ 1.6 km.)

4 A gyroscope has a moment of inertia of 0.01 kg m^2 about its axis of rotation and is set in motion by pulling a light string of length 0.5 m wrapped round the axis.

(i) Find the work done when the string is pulled off the axis with a constant force of 50 N.

(ii) Hence calculate the angular speed given to the gyroscope.

Using integration in moment of inertia calculations

The moment of inertia of a rigid body about an axis is given by

$$I = \sum_p m_p r_p^2 .$$

The sum is calculated over all particles of the body and m_p denotes the mass of a typical particle which is a fixed perpendicular distance, r_p, from the axis. The axis can be anywhere, even outside the body, so long as r_p is constant for each particle, which is therefore restricted to motion in a circle of radius r_p relative to the axis.

You might have guessed that calculus methods are required to work out most moments of inertia. These are very similar to those you have used before where sums are involved, namely: subdivide the body into elementary parts for which you know the moment of inertia and then sum the parts.

EXAMPLE 3.3

Calculate the moment of inertia of a uniform circular disc of radius r, thickness t and mass M about an axis through its centre perpendicular to its plane.

SOLUTION

Decide on appropriate elements.

The disc is divided into elementary rings. A typical ring has radius x, width δx and thickness t. Its volume is approximately $(2\pi x \delta x) \times t = 2\pi t x \delta x$.

It is useful to use the density, ρ, of the disc so that the mass of each part can be obtained. It can be written in terms of M at the end of the calculation.

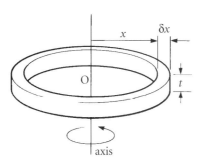

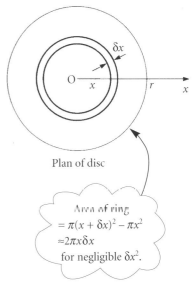

Plan of disc

Figure 3.7

Find the mass of a typical element in terms of the density.

The mass of the ring is then approximately

$$\delta m = (2\pi t x \delta x) \times \rho$$
$$= 2\pi t \rho x \delta x.$$

Area of ring
$= \pi(x + \delta x)^2 - \pi x^2$
$\approx 2\pi x \delta x$
for negligible δx^2.

For small δx every particle of such a ring is approximately the same distance, x, from the axis. The moment of inertia of the ring about the axis is therefore approximately

Determine the moment of inertia of the element about the axis.

$$\delta m x^2 = (2\pi t \rho x \delta x) x^2$$
$$= 2\pi t \rho x^3 \delta x$$

and the moment of inertia of the whole disc about the axis is approximately

Sum for all elements.

$$I = \sum (2\pi t \rho x^3 \delta x)$$
$$= 2\pi t \rho \sum (x^3 \delta x) \quad \text{(since } \rho \text{ and } t \text{ are the same for all rings).}$$

In the limit as $\delta x \to 0$, this gives

Write as an integral.

$$I = 2\pi t \rho \int_0^r x^3 \, \mathrm{d}x$$

Evaluate the integral.

$$\Rightarrow \quad I = 2\pi t \rho \left[\frac{x^4}{4} \right]_0^r$$

Note the limits: x takes values between 0 and r.

$$= \tfrac{1}{2}\pi t \rho r^4.$$

It is now necessary to replace ρ in terms of the mass of the disc, which has volume $\pi r^2 t$, so

Substitute for the density.

$$M = \pi r^2 t \rho.$$

Hence the moment of inertia of a disc about a perpendicular axis through its centre is

$$I = \tfrac{1}{2}(\pi t \rho r^2) r^2$$

or you could write
$$\frac{I}{M} = \frac{\pi t \rho r^4}{2\pi r^2 t \rho} = \tfrac{1}{2} r^2.$$

$$\Rightarrow \quad I = \tfrac{1}{2} M r^2.$$

The following points are worth noting at this stage.

- The moment of inertia of the disc ($\tfrac{1}{2} M r^2$) is less than the moment of inertia (Mr^2) of a ring of the same mass and radius because most of the matter in the disc is nearer the axis.
- The thickness of the disc does not appear in the equation. The disc could be a solid cylinder of any length and the same formula would hold so long as the axis of rotation is the axis of the cylinder. Of course, the moment of inertia of a cylinder is greater than that of a thin disc of the same radius and density, but only because the mass is greater.
- Using the same argument, the moment of inertia of a hollow cylinder of radius r about its axis has the same form as that of the ring, that is Mr^2. Each particle of the cylinder is the same distance, r, from the axis.
- The radius of gyration of the disc about this axis is $\dfrac{r}{\sqrt{2}}$. A ring of the same mass and moment of inertia would have a radius of $\dfrac{r}{\sqrt{2}}$.

EXAMPLE 3.4

Find the moment of inertia of a thin rod of length *2a* and mass *M* about an axis through its centre and perpendicular to the rod.

SOLUTION

Imagine that the rod is subdivided into small elements of width δx. Assume that the area, *A*, of a cross-section of the rod is so small that every point on it can be regarded as being the same distance from the axis. Then the only variable is the distance *x* of the elementary portion of the rod from the axis.

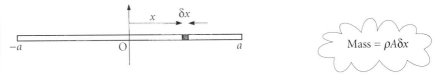

Figure 3.8

The mass of the element is $\rho A \delta x$, where ρ is the density, and its moment of inertia about the axis is approximately $(\rho A \delta x)x^2 = \rho A x^2 \delta x$.

The moment of inertia of the rod about the axis is therefore approximately $\sum \rho A x^2 \delta x$. In the limit as $\delta x \to 0$ this gives

$$I = \int_{-a}^{a} \rho A x^2 \, dx$$

$$= \rho A \int_{-a}^{a} x^2 \, dx$$

$$\Rightarrow \quad I = \rho A \left[\frac{x^3}{3} \right]_{-a}^{a}$$

$$= \frac{\rho A}{3}[a^3 - (-a)^3]$$

$$= \tfrac{2}{3} \rho A a^3.$$

The mass of the rod is $M = 2aA\rho = 2\rho Aa$. Hence the moment of inertia of a rod about a perpendicular axis through its centre is

$$I = \tfrac{1}{3}(2\rho Aa)a^2$$

$$= \tfrac{1}{3}Ma^2$$

or write

$$\frac{I}{M} = \frac{2\rho Aa^3}{3 \times 2\rho Aa} = \frac{1}{3}a^2$$

Once the moment of inertia of a body such as a rod or a disc is known, it can be used to find moments of inertia of other bodies.

For example, the thin rectangular lamina shown in figure 3.9 can be thought of as the sum of a large number of elementary rods.

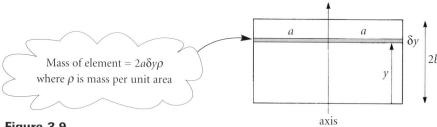

Mass of element = $2a\delta y\rho$
where ρ is mass per unit area

Figure 3.9

The mass of the elementary rod shown is $(2a\delta y)\rho$, where ρ is now the mass per unit area of the lamina. The moment of inertia of the elementary rod about the axis is then

$$\tfrac{1}{3}(2a\rho\delta y)a^2 = \tfrac{2}{3}a^3\rho\delta y$$

So the moment of inertia of the rectangular lamina about an axis of symmetry in its plane is

$$I = \int_0^{2b} \tfrac{2}{3}a^3\rho \, dy$$
$$= \tfrac{2}{3}a^3\rho \int_0^{2b} dy$$
$$= \tfrac{2}{3}a^3\rho 2b$$
$$= \tfrac{4}{3}ab\rho a^2.$$

But the mass of the lamina is $M = 4ab\rho$. Hence

$$I = \tfrac{1}{3}Ma^2.$$

Notice that this is independent of b and is in the same form as the moment of inertia of a thin rod about the axis. It is another case where the body is extended in the direction of the axis, leading to the same expression for the moment of inertia although, of course, the mass is greater.

Moments of inertia of selected uniform bodies

	Body of mass M	Axis	Moment of inertia
	Hoop or hollow cylinder of radius r	Through centre perpendicular to circular cross-section	Mr^2
	Disc or solid cylinder, of radius r	Through centre perpendicular to circular cross-section	$\frac{1}{2}Mr^2$
	Thin rod of length $2l$	Through centre perpendicular to rod	$\frac{1}{3}Ml^2$
	Rectangular lamina	Edge perpendicular to sides of length $2l$	$\frac{4}{3}Ml^2$
	Solid sphere of radius r	Diameter	$\frac{2}{5}Mr^2$

Dividing hollow bodies into elements

When a three-dimensional body is divided into elements, you should take care when deciding the 'width' of a typical element. Figure 3.10 shows a typical element, which you might always have considered to be approximately cylindrical. This is appropriate for a *solid body*, but not for a *surface*, especially near a point where it crosses the x axis. Also, because the mass depends on the surface area rather than the volume, a more appropriate approximation for a *thin shell* is to treat the element as part of a hollow cone.

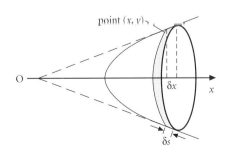

Figure 3.10

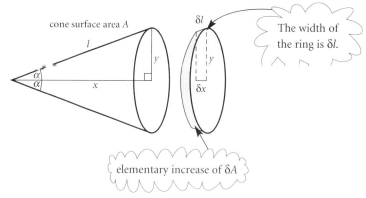

cone surface area A

The width of the ring is δl.

elementary increase of δA

Figure 3.11

For a small increase in the height, the surface area increases by $\delta A = 2\pi y \delta l$ or $2\pi r \delta l = 2\pi l \sin \alpha \, \delta l$ in this case. It translates into $2\pi y \delta s$ for any surface of revolution such as the one in figure 3.10.

The moment of inertia of a uniform hollow cone about its axis

You can use the result above to find the moment of inertia of the hollow cone about its axis. It is

$$\int_0^l \sigma 2\pi l \sin \alpha \, \mathrm{d}l)r^2 = \int_0^l \sigma 2\pi l \sin \alpha \, \mathrm{d}l (l \sin \alpha)^2 \quad (\sigma \text{ is the mass per unit area})$$

$$= 2\sigma\pi \sin^3 \alpha \int_0^l l^3 \mathrm{d}l$$

$$= \tfrac{1}{2}\sigma\pi \sin^3 \alpha \, l^4$$

$$= \tfrac{1}{2}(\sigma \pi l^2 \sin\alpha)l^2 \sin^2 \alpha$$

$$= \tfrac{1}{2}Mr^2 \qquad\qquad (M = \sigma A \text{ and } r = l \sin \alpha).$$

Combining bodies

When a rigid body has several parts, its moment of inertia about an axis can be found by adding the moments of inertia of the separate parts about the same axis. This is a direct consequence of the definition of the moment of inertia as a sum taken over all particles of the body; it doesn't matter if the sum is taken separately for different groups of particles. The next example illustrates this principle.

EXAMPLE 3.5

A wheel of mass M has been strengthened using a metal ring. It consists of a uniform disc of radius r and mass σ per unit area surrounded by a uniform solid ring (the rim) of radius r, negligible width, and mass $5r\sigma$ per unit length.

(i) Find the mass of the two parts of the wheel in terms of M.

(ii) Write down the moment of inertia of each part about the axle of the wheel.

(iii) Find the kinetic energy when the wheel is rotating with an angular speed ω.

(iv) Write this kinetic energy as a percentage of the kinetic energy of a hoop with the same mass and radius rotating at the same angular speed.

SOLUTION

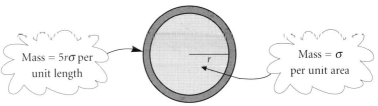

Mass = $5r\sigma$ per unit length

r

Mass = σ per unit area

Figure 3.12

(i) The area of the disc is πr^2, so its mass is $M_1 = \sigma \pi r^2$.
The length of the ring is $2\pi r$, so its mass is

$$M_2 = 2\pi r(5r\sigma)$$
$$= 10\,\sigma\pi r^2.$$

Hence $\quad M = 11\,\sigma\pi r^2$

$$\Rightarrow \quad M_1 = \frac{M}{11} \text{ and } M_2 = \frac{10M}{11}$$

(ii) The moment of inertia of the inside disc about the axle is

$$I_1 = \tfrac{1}{2}M_1 r^2$$
$$= \frac{Mr^2}{22}$$

The moment of inertia of the rim about the axle is

$$I_2 = M_2 r^2$$
$$= \frac{10\,Mr^2}{11}$$

(iii) The kinetic energy of the wheel is $\tfrac{1}{2}I\omega^2$, where $I = I_1 + I_2$.

$$I_1 + I_2 = \frac{Mr^2}{22} + \frac{10\,Mr^2}{11}$$
$$= \frac{21}{22}Mr^2$$

$$\Rightarrow \quad \text{kinetic energy} = \tfrac{1}{2}I\omega^2 = \frac{21}{44}Mr^2\omega^2$$

(iv) The moment of inertia of the hoop about its axis is Mr^2, so its kinetic energy is $\tfrac{1}{2}Mr^2\omega^2$.

The kinetic energy of the wheel is $\dfrac{21}{22} \times 100\%$ of the kinetic energy of the hoop, namely 95.5%.

Dividing regular bodies

You have already met the idea of elongating bodies in the direction of the axis. The elongated body is formed by combining identical elementary parts which all have the same moment of inertia about the axis. Conversely, when a body can be divided into two or more parts which obviously have the same moment of inertia about a given axis, it is possible to calculate the moments of inertia of the parts quite easily. For example, a sphere can be divided into two hemispheres using any plane through its centre. To each particle P_1 in one half there corresponds a similarly placed particle P_2 in the other half with the same moment of inertia about the axis. These are shown in figure 3.13.

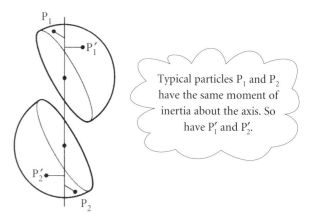

Typical particles P_1 and P_2 have the same moment of inertia about the axis. So have P_1' and P_2'.

Figure 3.13

The moment of inertia of each hemisphere about the axis is therefore

$$\tfrac{1}{2}\left(\tfrac{2}{5}Mr^2\right) = \tfrac{2}{5}\left(\frac{M}{2}\right)r^2$$
$$= \tfrac{2}{5}M_1 r^2$$

where M_1 is the mass of each hemisphere. Again, the form of the expression does not change although the mass does.

Conservation of energy

Knowing the moment of inertia of a rotating body enables you to solve some rotation problems purely by energy methods.

EXAMPLE 3.6

A uniform thin rod AB of mass m and length $2a$ has a particle of mass M attached at B and is hinged at its centre O so that it rotates freely in a vertical plane. The rod is held horizontally and released.

(i) Show the moment of inertia of the system about the hinge is $\tfrac{4}{3}Ma^2$.

(ii) Find the angular speed when the rod is vertical.

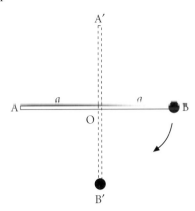

Figure 3.14

SOLUTION

(i) The moment of inertia of the rod alone is $\frac{1}{3}Ma^2$ (see page 85).
The moment of inertia of the particle about the axis is Ma^2.
So the total moment of inertia of the system about the axis is

$$I = Ma^2 + \tfrac{1}{3}Ma^2$$
$$= \tfrac{4}{3}Ma^2$$

(ii) When in the vertical position, the gain in kinetic energy is:

$$\tfrac{1}{2}I\omega^2 = \tfrac{2}{3}Ma^2\omega^2.$$

The loss in potential energy arises from the descent of the mass at B and is given by Mga.
Hence, by conservation of energy:

$$\tfrac{2}{3}Ma^2\omega^2 = Mga$$

$$\Rightarrow \qquad \omega = \sqrt{\frac{3g}{2a}}.$$

> Note that there is no change in the potential energy of the rod during the rotation because the axis is through its centre of mass. In the next chapter you will meet the case where this is not so.

1 A uniform thin rod OA of mass M and length $2a$ is hinged at one end O so that it can rotate freely about an axis through O perpendicular to OA. An element of the rod of length δx is situated a distance x from O. ρ is the mass per unit length of the rod.

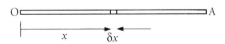

(i) Write down the mass of the element.
(ii) Write down the moment of inertia of the element about the axis.
(iii) Form a suitable integral to calculate the moment of inertia of the rod about the axis and evaluate it.

(iv) Write M in terms of a and ρ and hence show that the moment of inertia of the rod about the axis is $\frac{4}{3}Ma^2$.

(v) Use your result to find the moment of inertia of a uniform rectangular lamina of width $2a$ about an axis along the edge which is perpendicular to this width.

2 A door of mass 35 kg and width 0.8 m is slammed shut with an angular speed of 2.5 rad s^{-1}.

(i) By modelling the door as a lamina and dividing it into vertical strips, or otherwise, find its moment of inertia about the axis through the hinges.

(ii) Find the amount of energy dissipated when the door shuts.

3 A uniform solid sphere has radius r, density ρ and centre at the origin. It is divided into elementary discs perpendicular to the x axis so that a typical disc has thickness δx, radius y and centre at $(x, 0)$, as shown in the diagram.

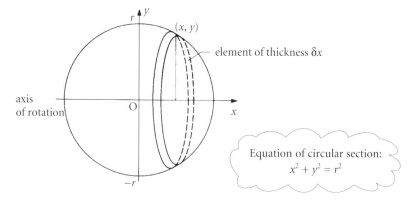

element of thickness δx

axis of rotation

Equation of circular section:
$x^2 + y^2 = r^2$

(i) Write down an expression for the mass of a typical disc.

(ii) Show that the moment of inertia of the sphere about the x axis is given by

$$I = \int_{-r}^{r} \tfrac{1}{2}\rho\pi y^4 \mathrm{d}x$$

(iii) Substitute an expression for y^2 in terms of x and so evaluate this integral.

(iv) Write the mass, M, of the sphere in terms of ρ, π and r and hence show that the moment of inertia of the sphere about a diameter is given by $\frac{2}{5}Mr^2$.

(v) Suggest a suitable integral for finding the moment of inertia of any solid of revolution about the x axis.

4 (i) Assume the Earth is a uniform sphere of mass 6×10^{24} kg and radius 6400 km.

Use the result of Question 3 part **(iv)** to estimate its moment of inertia and its kinetic energy of rotation about its axis.

Given that the density of the Earth increases towards the centre, how would this compare with the true value?

(ii) Assume the moon is a uniform sphere of mass 7.5×10^{22} kg and radius 1700 km and that it rotates once every 28 days.
Estimate its kinetic energy of rotation about its axis.

(iii) Now assume the moon is a particle which rotates round the centre of the Earth once every 28 days in a circle of radius 3.85×10^5 km.
Find its kinetic energy due to this motion.

(iv) Find the ratio of the kinetic energy of the Earth to the total kinetic energy of the moon (not including their motion round the sun).

5 A potter is throwing clay on a wheel which turns at a constant rate. It starts as a solid cylinder of radius r and height h and gradually changes into a jar with the cross-section shown in the diagram.

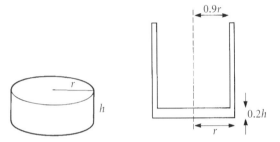

Assume the mass, M kg, and the density of the clay are constant.

(i) Find an expression for the density of the clay.

(ii) Find the height, in terms of h, of the jar when the thickness of the base is $0.2h$ and the inside radius is $0.9r$.

(iii) Assuming the jar is a solid cylinder with another removed from the inside, find its moment of inertia about its axis of rotation in terms of M and r.

(iv) Find the ratio of the kinetic energy of the jar to that of the original cylinder.

6 In order to calculate its moment of inertia about a diameter, a hollow sphere is divided into thin rings as shown. Its mass per unit area is σ.

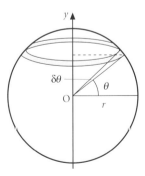

(i) Give an expression for the surface area of the typical ring shown in the diagram and hence an expression for its moment of inertia about the y axis.

(ii) Use integration to find the moment of inertia about its diameter of a hollow sphere of mass M and radius r.

Further calculations of moments of inertia

Two important theorems are useful in the calculation of moments of inertia.

The perpendicular axes theorem

You know the moment of inertia of a rectangular lamina about an axis of symmetry in its plane. The moments of inertia of the lamina in figure 3.15 are

$$I_y = \tfrac{1}{3}Ma^2 \quad \text{about the } y \text{ axis (AB has length } 2a)$$

and similarly

$$I_x = \tfrac{1}{3}Mb^2 \quad \text{about the } x \text{ axis (BC has length } 2b)$$

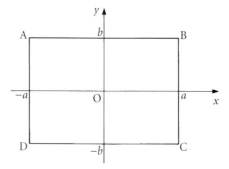

Figure 3.15

But what is its moment of inertia about the z axis through O perpendicular to its plane? This can be found by applying a very useful result known as the perpendicular axes theorem for a lamina, which can be stated as follows.

- The moment of inertia of a lamina about an axis which is perpendicular to the plane of the lamina and passes through a point O in its plane, is equal to the sum of the moments of inertia about two perpendicular axes in the plane of the lamina which also pass through O.

Using the notation above, $I_z = I_x + I_y$.

You will see from the following proof that it is essential for the body to be a lamina.

A particle P of mass m situated at the point (x, y) of any lamina in the xy plane is a distance r from O (and hence the z axis), where $r^2 = x^2 + y^2$ (see figure 3.16).

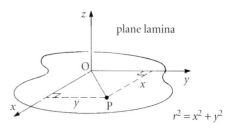

Figure 3.16

The moment of inertia of P about the z axis through O is therefore $m(x^2 + y^2)$. Hence the moment of inertia of the whole lamina about the z axis is

$$I_z = \sum m(x^2 + y^2)$$
$$= \sum mx^2 + \sum my^2$$

But $\sum mx^2$ is the moment of inertia, I_y, about the y axis and $\sum my^2$ is the moment of inertia, I_x, about the x axis. It follows that

$$I_z = I_x + I_y.$$

This is true for any lamina in the xy plane.

Note that the origin and the x and y axes must always be in the plane of the lamina.

For the rectangle this gives

$$I_z = \tfrac{1}{3}Ma^2 + \tfrac{1}{3}Mb^2$$
$$= \tfrac{1}{3}M(a^2 + b^2) \quad \text{or} \quad \tfrac{1}{3}Md^2$$

where d is the distance from the centre to a vertex of the rectangle.

EXAMPLE 3.7

Use the perpendicular axes theorem to find the moment of inertia of a thin circular disc of radius r about a diameter.

SOLUTION

By symmetry the moment of inertia about every diameter is the same, say I_d. This means that, when the disc is in the xy plane with its centre at the origin,

$$I_x = I_y = I_d.$$

But I_z is the moment of inertia about the axis through O perpendicular to the disc and this is $\tfrac{1}{2}Mr^2$. Hence

$$\tfrac{1}{2}Mr^2 = I_x + I_y$$
$$= 2I_d$$
$$\Rightarrow \quad I_d = \tfrac{1}{4}Mr^2$$

$I_x = I_y$ and $I_z = \tfrac{1}{2}Mr^2$

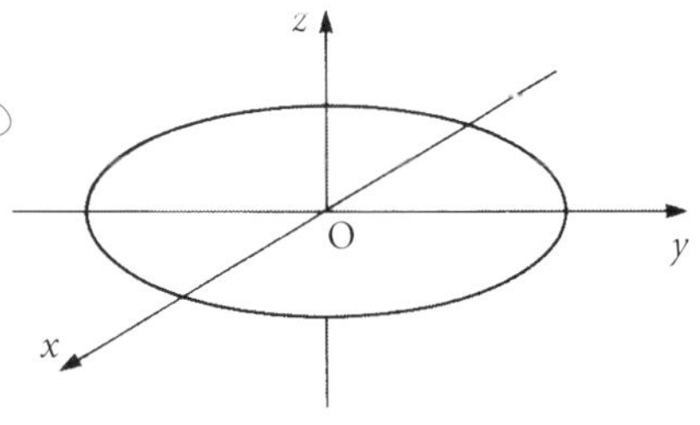

Figure 3.17

The parallel axes theorem

In many circumstances, for example when a disc rotates about a diameter, or when two rigid bodies are combined to form another, the axis of rotation may not be in the most convenient position for the calculation of a moment of inertia. The parallel axes theorem can be used in these circumstances because it gives a relationship between the moments of inertia of the same rigid body about different parallel axes.

The theorem can be stated as follows.

- The moment of inertia of a rigid body of mass M about a fixed axis through a point A is equal to its moment of inertia about a parallel axis through its centre of mass G plus Md^2, where d is the perpendicular distance between the axes:

$$I_A = I_G + Md^2$$

Figure 3.18 shows two parallel axes which are a fixed distance, d, apart. The axis GR passes through G and the other axis, AQ, passes through a point A such that AG is perpendicular to both axes and hence of length d. The moments of inertia of the body about these two axes are denoted by I_G and I_A. Consider a typical particle P of mass m_p and suppose that the plane through P perpendicular to the two axes meets GR at O and AQ at S as shown. Then OS = GA = d.

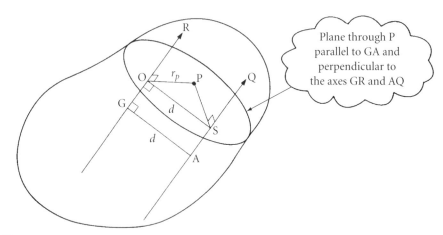

Figure 3.18

Figure 3.19 shows the plane through P. Co-ordinate axes have been taken through O parallel and perpendicular to OS. The co-ordinates of P relative to these axes are (x_p, y_p) and $r_p^2 = x_p^2 + y_p^2$ as usual.

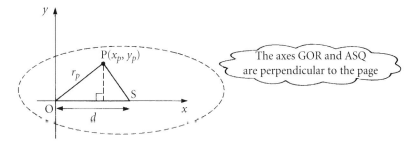

Figure 3.19

$$PS^2 = (d - x_p)^2 + y_p^2$$
$$= x_p^2 + y_p^2 + d^2 - 2dx_p$$
$$= r_p^2 + d^2 - 2dx_p.$$

The moment of inertia of the particle P about the axis ASQ is

$$m_p PS^2 = m_p (r_p^2 + d^2 - 2dx_p).$$

The moment of inertia of the whole body about the axis AQ is

$$I_A = \sum m_p (r_p^2 + d^2 - 2dx_p) \quad \text{(summed over all particles P)}$$
$$= \sum m_p r_p^2 + \sum m_p d^2 - \sum 2dm_p x_p$$
$$= I_G + Md^2 - 2d \sum m_p x_p$$

Remember, r_p is the distance of P from the axis GR.

Now x_p is equal to the x co-ordinate of P relative to a new three-dimensional co-ordinate system with origin at G and GA as its x axis (see figure 3.20).

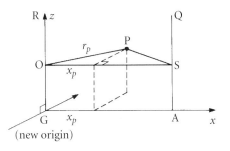

Figure 3.20

But, by the definition of the centre of mass, $\sum m_p x_p = M\bar{x}$ and $\bar{x}$ is zero because G is at the origin. So $2d \sum m_p x_p = 0$. Hence

$$I_A = I_G + Md^2.$$

The parallel axes theorem can be used to extend your repertoire of moments of inertia, but remember that one of the axes must be through the centre of mass.

A consequence of this theorem is that the moment of inertia, and hence also the rotational kinetic energy, are least when the axis is through G. However, the minimum kinetic energy possible for a given body and a given value of ω depends on the orientation of the axis.

EXAMPLE 3.8

Use the parallel axes theorem to find the moments of inertia of

(i) a thin uniform rod of mass M and length h about a perpendicular axis through its end

(ii) a thin uniform solid disc of mass M and radius r about

    (a) an axis perpendicular to its plane through a point on its circumference

    (b) a tangent.

(iii) Which of the above is equally applicable to a solid cylinder?

SOLUTION

(i) For the rod $I_{\mathrm{G}} = \frac{1}{3}M\left(\frac{h}{2}\right)^2$ and the axes are a distance $\frac{h}{2}$ apart. Hence

$$I_{\mathrm{A}} = I_{\mathrm{G}} + M\left(\frac{h}{2}\right)^2$$

$$= \frac{1}{3}M\left(\frac{h}{2}\right)^2 + M\left(\frac{h}{2}\right)^2$$

$$= \frac{1}{3}Mh^2.$$

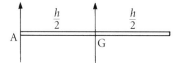

Figure 3.21

(ii) (a) In this case $I_{\mathrm{G}} = \frac{1}{2}Mr^2$ and the axes are a distance r apart.

    Hence $\quad I_{\mathrm{A}} = I_{\mathrm{G}} + Mr^2$

$$= \frac{1}{2}Mr^2 + Mr^2$$

$$= \frac{3}{2}Mr^2$$

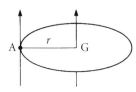

Figure 3.22

(b) Now $\quad I_{\mathrm{G}} = \frac{1}{4}Mr^2$

$$\Rightarrow \quad I_{\mathrm{A}} = \frac{1}{4}Mr^2 + Mr^2$$

$$= \frac{5}{4}Mr^2.$$

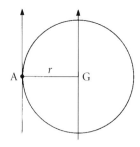

Figure 3.23

(iii) The result is applicable to a cylinder so long as this is formed by elongating the body in a direction parallel to the axis of rotation. It therefore applies in part **(ii)(a)** but not in the other cases.

The next example illustrates how the parallel axes theorem can be used in conjunction with calculus methods to find the moment of inertia of a solid, in this case a cylinder, about an axis which is not an axis of symmetry.

EXAMPLE 3.9

Find the moment of inertia of a uniform solid cylinder of mass M, radius r and height h about an axis which is perpendicular to the axis of the cylinder and which passes through the centre of one end.

SOLUTION

Choose axes as shown in figure 3.24 so that the required moment of inertia is about the x axis. Let ρ be the density of the cylinder, so that $M = \pi r^2 h \rho$. Subdivide the cylinder into elementary discs as shown.

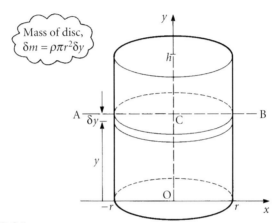

Figure 3.24

A typical disc has thickness δy and centre at $C(0, y)$.

Its mass δm is approximately $\rho \pi r^2 \delta y$.

The moment of inertia of the element about an axis through C parallel to the x axis (i.e. a diameter) is $\frac{1}{4} \delta m r^2$.

C is the centre of mass of the disc, so by the parallel axes theorem, its moment of inertia about the x axis is

$$\tfrac{1}{4}\delta m r^2 + \delta m y^2 = \tfrac{1}{4}(\rho \pi r^2 \delta y)r^2 + (\rho \pi r^2 \delta y)y^2$$
$$= \tfrac{1}{4}\rho \pi r^2 (r^2 + 4y^2)\delta y.$$

For the whole cylinder, the moment of inertia about the x axis, I_x, is approximately

$$\sum \tfrac{1}{4}\rho \pi r^2 (r^2 + 4y^2)\delta y = \tfrac{1}{4}\rho \pi r^2 \sum (r^2 + 4y^2)\delta y.$$

In the limit as $\delta y \to 0$, this gives

$$I_x = \tfrac{1}{4}\rho\pi r^2 \int_0^h (r^2 + 4y^2)\,\mathrm{d}y$$

$$= \tfrac{1}{4}\rho\pi r^2 \left[r^2 y + 4\frac{y^3}{3} \right]_0^h$$

$$= \tfrac{1}{4}\rho\pi r^4 h + \tfrac{1}{3}\rho\pi r^2 h^3$$

$$= \tfrac{1}{4}M r^2 + \tfrac{1}{3}M h^2 \quad (M = \rho\pi r^2 h).$$

It is interesting to note that this has the same form as the sum of the moments of inertia of a disc of radius r about its diameter and a rod of length h about a perpendicular axis through its end: $h = 0$ gives the disc and $r = 0$ gives the rod.

Summary

- $I = \Sigma\, mr^2$
- Perpendicular axes theorem: $I_z = I_x + I_y$ for a lamina only.
- Parallel axes theorem: $I_A = I_G + Md^2$

$$= I_G + M(\mathrm{AG})^2$$

when G is the centre of mass and AG is perpendicular to the axes.

EXERCISE 3C

1 The model shown in the diagram is made up of light rods of length a and beads of mass m.

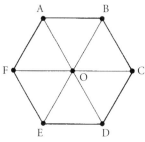

(i) Calculate in terms of m and a its moment of inertia about the axis
   (a) through O perpendicular to the plane ABCDEF
   (b) AOD
   (c) through O and the mid-point of BC.
(ii) Verify that the perpendicular axes theorem is true for this model.
(iii) Use the results of part (i) and the parallel axes theorem to find the moment of inertia about
   (a) an axis through A perpendicular to the plane ABCDEF
   (b) BC.
   Check your answers by considering the moments of inertia for individual beads.

2 An odd number $(2n + 1)$ of beads each of mass m and negligible size are joined in a straight line by equal light rods of length a. The total mass of the model is M.

(i) Show that the moment of inertia I_M about an axis perpendicular to the line through the middle bead is $\dfrac{n}{3}(n+1)Ma^2$.

$$\left(\text{Hint: } \sum_{r=1}^{n} r^2 = \frac{n}{6}(n+1)(2n+1) \right)$$

(ii) Use the parallel axes theorem to show that the moment of inertia I_E about the end bead is given by $I_E = I_M + n^2 Ma^2$.
Hence find I_E.

(iii) Verify that the answer to part (ii) is the same as the result obtained from first principles.

(iv) Write down the length of the line of beads. The number of rods now increases and the length of each rod decreases in such a way that the total length is always $2l$. Show that in the limit as $n \to \infty$ and $a \to 0$, the moments of inertia you found in parts (i) and (ii) approach the equivalent moments of inertia for a rod of mass M and length $2l$.

3 The following table can be completed by using the perpendicular and parallel axes theorems and the idea of elongating the body parallel to the axis. Copy and complete it. You might find it useful to keep a copy for future reference.

Uniform body of mass M	Axis	Moment of inertia
Hoop radius r	Through centre $\perp$ to plane	Mr^2
Hollow cylinder radius r	Through centre $\perp$ to circular cross-section	
Thin ring radius r	Diameter	
Thin ring radius r	Through edge $\perp$ to plane	
Thin ring radius r	Tangent	
Disc of radius r	Through centre $\perp$ to plane	$\frac{1}{2}Mr^2$
Solid cylinder radius r	Through centre $\perp$ to circular cross-section	

Uniform body of mass M	Axis	Moment of inertia
Thin disc radius r	Diameter	
Thin disc radius r	Through edge $\perp$ to disc	
Thin disc radius r	Tangent	
Thin rod	Parallel to rod at distance d	Md^2
Thin rod of length $2l$	Through centre $\perp$ to rod	$\frac{1}{3}Ml^2$
Thin rod of length $2l$	Through end $\perp$ to rod	
Rectangular lamina	In plane, through centre $\perp$ to sides length $2l$	$\frac{1}{3}Ml^2$
Rectangular lamina	Edge $\perp$ to sides length $2l$	
Rectangular lamina sides $2a$ and $2b$	Through centre $\perp$ to plane	
Rectangular block sides $2a$, $2b$ and $2c$	Through centre parallel to sides of length $2c$	
Solid sphere radius r	Diameter	$\frac{2}{5}Mr^2$
Solid sphere radius r	Tangent	
Hollow sphere radius r	Diameter	$\frac{2}{3}Mr^2$
Hollow sphere radius r	Tangent	

4 (i) Write down the moment of inertia of a thin disc of mass M and radius r about an axis through its centre perpendicular to its plane.

The disc is divided into equal sectors as shown in the diagrams below.

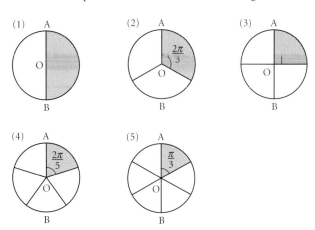

(ii) By using ideas of symmetry, find the moments of inertia of the shaded sectors about axes through O perpendicular to their planes
   (a) in terms of M
   (b) in terms of the mass m of the particular sector.
(iii) Write down the moment of inertia of the disc about its diameter AB. Symmetry can still be used to find the moments of inertia of some of the shaded sectors about OA. Write down the moments of inertia of those that are possible and explain why the others cannot be found in this way.

5 The surface of a uniform hollow sphere of mass M and radius r can be represented in three dimensions by the equation:

$$x^2 + y^2 + z^2 = r^2.$$

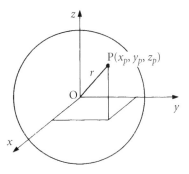

(i) Write down the distance from the z axis of a typical particle of mass m_p situated at the point (x_p, y_p, z_p) and hence show that the moment of inertia of the whole sphere about the z axis is given by

$$I_z = \sum m_p (x_p^2 + y_p^2).$$

(ii) Write down similar equations for the moments of inertia, I_x and I_y, of the sphere about the x axis and the y axis.

(iii) The moment of inertia of the sphere about any diameter is I. Explain why $3I = I_x + I_y + I_z$ and hence show that $I = \frac{2}{5}Mr^2$, as given in question 3.

6 A uniform thin rod AB of mass M and length $2a$ is free to rotate about an axis through its centre O which is inclined at an angle α to the rod AB as shown.

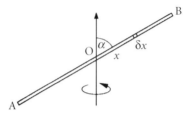

An element of the rod of length δx is situated a distance x from O. ρ is the mass per unit length of the rod.

(i) Write down the mass of the element.

(ii) Write down the moment of inertia of the element about the axis.

(iii) Form a suitable integral to calculate the moment of inertia of the rod about the axis and evaluate it.

(iv) Write M in terms of a and ρ and hence show that the moment of inertia of the rod about the axis is the same as that of a rod of the same mass and of length $2a \sin \alpha$ which is perpendicular to the axis. Check your answer in the cases $\alpha = \frac{\pi}{2}$ and $\alpha = 0$.

(v) Use your result to find the moment of inertia of a parallelogram about an axis in its plane which passes through its centre and bisects a side of length $2a$, as shown in the diagram.

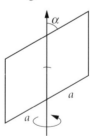

(vi) How will the moment of inertia of any lamina be affected by a shearing in the direction of the axis of rotation as shown in the diagram?

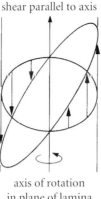

shear parallel to axis

axis of rotation
in plane of lamina

7 A lamina of mass M in the form of an isosceles triangle OAB is shown in the diagram. OA = OB, AB = $2a$ and the height OC = h. The lamina is divided into elementary strips of width δx parallel to AB as shown.

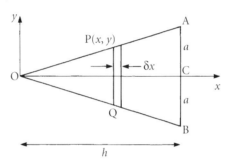

(i) Write down the mass of a typical strip PQ of width δx in terms of σ, the mass per unit area of the lamina, and the co-ordinates (x, y) of P.

(ii) By treating the strip as a thin rod, write down its moment of inertia about the x axis.

(iii) Write y in terms of x and form an integral to find the moment of inertia of the triangle about the x axis.

(iv) Find the moment of inertia about the x axis in terms of M and a.

(v) Give a reason why the moment of inertia of the same elementary strip about the y axis is $2x^2\sigma y\delta x$.

(vi) Find the moment of inertia of the triangle about the y axis.

(vii) Use the perpendicular axes theorem to find the moment of inertia of the triangle about an axis through O perpendicular to its plane.

(viii) Use the parallel axes theorem to find the moment of inertia of the triangle about an axis perpendicular to its plane through its centre of mass.

8 (i) The arc of the circle AB shown in the diagram is of mass m and is symmetrical about the initial line $\theta = 0$. It is divided into elements of length $r\delta\theta$.

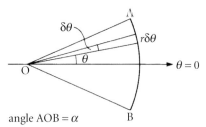

angle AOB $= \alpha$

Show by integration that its moment of inertia about the axis $\theta = 0$ is

$$\tfrac{1}{2}mr^2\left(1 - \frac{\sin\alpha}{\alpha}\right).$$

(ii) The sector of the circle shown in the diagram below is of mass M and radius a and it is symmetrical about the initial line $\theta = 0$. It is divided into elementary arcs of radius r and width δr.

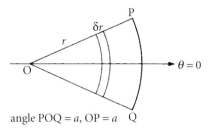

angle POQ $= a$, OP $= a$

Use the result of part **(i)** to show that its moment of inertia about the axis $\theta = 0$ is

$$\tfrac{1}{4}Ma^2\left(1 - \frac{\sin\alpha}{\alpha}\right).$$

9 A uniform solid cone of mass M, base radius r and height h is placed with its vertex at O and its axis of symmetry along the x axis, as shown. A typical elementary disc of thickness δx is at the point $P(x, y)$.

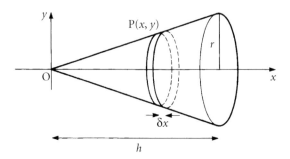

Use ρ for the density of the disc.

(i) Write down the approximate mass of the elementary disc in terms of y, ρ and δx.

(ii) Show that the moment of inertia of the disc about the x axis is approximately $\frac{1}{2}\pi\rho y^4\delta x$.

(iii) Form a suitable integral to find the moment of inertia of the cone about the x axis.

(iv) Write y in terms of x and evaluate the integral.

(v) Write the mass of the cone in terms of r, h and ρ and hence find the moment of inertia of the cone about the x axis.

10 The region between the parabola $y^2 = 4ax$, the x axis and the line $x = b$ is rotated completely about the x axis.

(i) Find the volume of revolution so formed and hence write its mass M in terms of its density ρ.

(ii) Use the method outlined in question 9 to calculate its moment of inertia about the x axis in terms of M and a.

11 The ellipse $\dfrac{x^2}{a^2} + \dfrac{y^2}{b^2} = 1$ is rotated completely about the x axis, forming a solid of revolution of mass M.

(i) Find the moment of inertia of the solid about the x axis in terms of M.

(ii) Write down a similar expression for the moment of inertia of the solid formed when the ellipse is rotated about the y axis.

(iii) Comment on your results.

12 Find by integration the moment of inertia of a uniform solid cone of mass M, height h and base radius r about an axis through its vertex perpendicular to its axis of symmetry.

13 A point O on a plane lamina is used as the origin in a system of co-ordinates and the lamina is in the xy plane. A typical particle, P, of the lamina has mass m and co-ordinates $(x, y, 0)$. I_z and I_x are the moments of inertia of the lamina about the z axis and the x axis respectively.

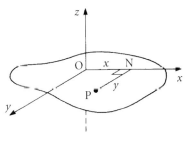

(i) Explain why $I_z = \Sigma m(x^2 + y^2)$ summed over all particles and write I_x in terms of another sum.

(ii) The lamina is now turned through an angle θ about the x axis.

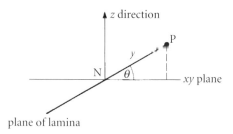

plane of lamina

By considering the new moment of inertia of the typical particle, P, about the z axis, show that the moment of inertia about the z axis of the lamina in its new position is given by

$$\sum m(x^2 + y^2 \cos^2 \theta)$$

and so is equal to $I_z - I_x \sin^2 \theta$.

(iii) A helicopter blade of mass m is modelled as a rectangle of length a and width b as shown in the photograph. One long edge, AB, is attached to the axle of the rotating mechanism and is a distance c from the axle. The blade can be turned about AB during flight.

Find expressions for the moment of inertia of the blade about the axle when AB is horizontal and the blade is

(a) horizontal

(b) inclined to the horizontal at an angle θ.

14 A uniform hollow sphere of mass, M, has internal radius a, external radius b, and density ρ.

(i) Find, in terms of ρ, a and b, expressions for the masses of solid spheres of radius a and b and their moments of inertia about a diameter.

(ii) Show that the moment of inertia of the hollow sphere about an axis through its centre is $\dfrac{8\pi\rho}{15}(b^5 - a^5)$.

(iii) The table shows a model of the Earth with different densities at different depths.

Distance from centre in km	Density in kg m^{-3}
<1250	13 000
1250–	10 000
3500–	5 500
5700–	4 000
6200–6400	2 900

Assuming the Earth is a sphere, use this model to find its moment of inertia about its axis.

(iv) The mean density of the Earth is 5500 kg m^{-3}. Show that when it is assumed to be a uniform sphere, the moment of inertia of the Earth about its axis is overestimated by about 12% compared with the above model.

15 (i) Use the result of question 14 (ii) to show that the moment of inertia about a diameter of a hollow sphere of mass M, internal radius a and external radius b is $\dfrac{2M(b^5 - a^5)}{5(b^3 - a^3)}$.

(ii) Verify that $b^5 - a^5 = (b - a)(b^4 + ab^3 + a^2b^2 + a^3b + a^4)$ and by factorising $(b^3 - a^3)$ in a similar way, find an alternative expression for the moment of inertia of the hollow sphere about its diameter.

(iii) Now let $a \to b$ and hence show that the moment of inertia about a diameter of a thin hollow sphere of radius b is $\frac{2}{3}Mb^2$.

16 A uniform circular disc has mass M_1, radius b and centre O. Cartesian axes (x, y, z) are chosen with the origin at O, the z axis normal to the plane of the disc and the x and y axes fixed along diameters.

(i) Prove that the moment of inertia I_z of the disc about the z axis is $\frac{1}{2}M_1b^2$. Hence, or otherwise, find the moments of inertia I_x and I_y about the x and y axes respectively.

You are given that the moment of inertia of a rod of length $2l$ and mass M_2 about an axis through its centre perpendicular to its length is $\frac{1}{3}M_2l^2$.

(ii) Show that the moment of inertia of a square lamina of mass M and side $2l$ about an axis through its centre perpendicular to its plane is $\frac{2}{3}Ml^2$.

A valve lifting device is made from a uniform circular disc of radius a with a square hole cut out, as shown in the diagram overleaf.

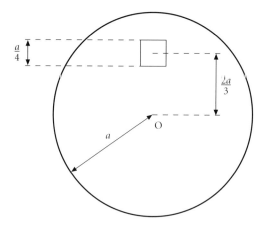

The hole has sides of length $\dfrac{a}{4}$ and the centre of the hole is a distance $\dfrac{2a}{3}$ from the centre O of the disc. The mass of the device is m.

(iii) Show that the moment of inertia I of the device about an axis perpendicular to its plane through the point O is given by

$$I = \left(\frac{8\pi - \frac{131}{288}}{16\pi - 1} \right) ma^2.$$

[MEI]

Bodies with variable density

Some bodies are made of several materials of differing densities. The moments of inertia of these can be found by dealing with each part separately (for example, see Exercise 3C, question 14). Others have densities which vary continuously and, provided the functions are relatively simple, calculus methods can be used to determine their moments of inertia.

EXAMPLE 3.10

A star is modelled as a sphere of radius a whose density is given in terms of the distance r from the centre by the function $\rho = \rho_0 \left(1 - \dfrac{r^2}{a^2} \right)$.

(i) Given that ρ_0 is constant, find the total mass M of the sphere.
(ii) Find its moment of inertia about a diameter.

SOLUTION

Imagine that the sphere is divided into elementary shells and a typical shell has radius r and thickness δr.

(i) The mass of the shell is

$$4\pi r^2 \rho \delta r = \frac{4\pi \rho_0}{a^2} (a^2 r^2 - r^4) \delta r.$$ ①

$$\Rightarrow \qquad M = \int_0^a \frac{4\pi\rho_0}{a^2}(a^2r^2 - r^4)\,dr$$

$$= \frac{4\pi\rho_0}{a^2}\left[a^2\frac{r^3}{3} - \frac{r^5}{5}\right]_0^a$$

$$= \frac{8\pi\rho_0}{15}a^3 \qquad \textcircled{2}$$

(ii) The moment of inertia of a hollow shell of mass m about a diameter is

$\frac{2}{3}mr^2$, so the moment of inertia of an elementary shell is

$$\frac{2}{3} \times \frac{4\pi\rho_0}{a^2}(a^2r^2 - r^4)\delta r \times r^2 \qquad \text{(from } \textcircled{1})$$

$$\Rightarrow \quad \text{moment of inertia of sphere} = \int_0^a \frac{8\pi\rho_0}{3a^2}(a^2r^4 - r^6)\,dr$$

$$= \frac{8\pi\rho_0}{3a^2}\left[a^2\frac{r^5}{5} - \frac{r^7}{7}\right]_0^a$$

$$= \frac{16\pi\rho_0}{105}a^5$$

$$= \frac{2}{7}Ma^2 \qquad \text{(from } \textcircled{2})$$

A baseball bat is thicker at one end than the other, but its thickness is always small compared with its length so it is possible to model it by a rod of varying density as illustrated in the next example.

EXAMPLE 3.11

A baseball bat has a uniform handle AB of length 0.36 m and mass $M_1 = 0.136$ kg. The remainder of the bat is modelled as a thin rod BC of length 0.7 m and mass per unit length $1.43(x^2 + x + 0.25)$ kg m^{-1}, where x is the distance from B. Assuming the handle can also be modelled as a thin rod, find

(i) the mass M kg of the bat
(ii) the distance of its centre of mass, G, from B
(iii) its moment of inertia about a perpendicular axis through B
(iv) its moment of inertia about a perpendicular axis through the end A.

Figure 3.25

SOLUTION

Figure 3.26 shows the essential features of the bat.

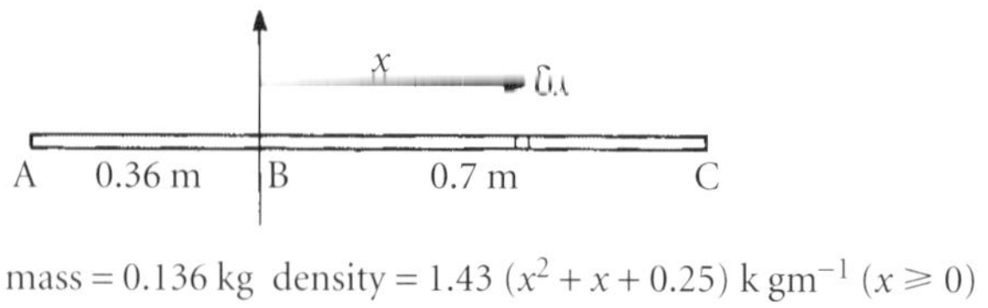

mass = 0.136 kg density = 1.43 $(x^2 + x + 0.25)$ k gm^{-1} $(x \geqslant 0)$

Figure 3.26

(i) The mass of an element of BC of length δx is $1.43(x^2 + x + 0.25)\delta x$ kg.

$\Rightarrow$ mass of BC $= \displaystyle\int_0^{0.7} 1.43(x^2 + x + 0.25) \, dx$ kg

$$= \left[1.43\left(\frac{x^3}{3} + \frac{x^2}{2} + 0.25x \right) \right]_0^{0.7} \text{kg}$$

$$= 0.764 \text{ kg}$$

$\Rightarrow$ Total mass $M = 0.764 + 0.136 = 0.900$ kg (to 3 significant figures)

(ii) To find the distance, $\bar{x}$, of G from B, take moments about an axis through B. Then

$$\left(\sum \delta m \right) \bar{x} = \sum (\delta mx) \quad \text{(summed for all particles of the bat).}$$

For AB $\displaystyle\sum (\delta mx) = -M_1 \times \tfrac{1}{2} \text{AB}$

$$= -0.136 \times 0.18$$

$$= -0.0245$$

and for BC $\displaystyle\sum (\delta mx) = \sum 1.43(x^2 + x + 0.25)x \, \delta x.$

In the limit as $\delta x \to 0$, this becomes

$$\int_0^{0.7} 1.43(x^2 + x + 0.25)x \, dx$$

$$= \int_0^{0.7} 1.43(x^3 + x^2 + 0.25x) \, dx$$

$$= 1.43 \left[\frac{x^4}{4} + \frac{x^3}{3} + 0.25\frac{x^2}{2} \right]_0^{0.7}$$

$$= 0.3369.$$

Combining AB and BC gives

$$0.9\bar{x} = -0.0245 + 0.3369$$

$\Rightarrow$ $0.9\bar{x} = 0.3124$

$$\bar{x} = 0.347.$$

The centre of mass is about 35 cm from B.

(iii) The moment of inertia, I_1, of the uniform rod AB about a perpendicular axis through its centre is $\frac{1}{3}M_1(0.18)^2$. So, by the parallel axes theorem, its moment of inertia about the end B is

$$I_1 = \frac{1}{3}M_1(0.18)^2 + M_1(0.18)^2$$

$$= \frac{4}{3}(0.136)(0.18)^2$$

$$= 0.0059 \text{ kg m}^2.$$

The moment of inertia, I_2, of the part BC about the axis through B is

$$I_2 = \lim_{\delta x \to 0}\left(\sum \delta m x^2\right)$$

$$= \int_0^{0.7} 1.43(x^2 + x + 0.25)x^2 dx$$

$$= \int_0^{0.7} 1.43(x^4 + x^3 + 0.25x^2)dx$$

$$= 1.43\left[\frac{x^5}{5} + \frac{x^4}{4} + 0.25\frac{x^3}{3}\right]_0^{0.7}$$

$$= 0.1748.$$

Hence: $I_1 + I_2 = 0.1807$

The moment of inertia of the bat about a perpendicular axis through B is about 0.18 kg m^2.

(iv) By the parallel axes theorem

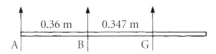

Figure 3.27

$$I_B = I_G + M(BG)^2 \qquad \longleftarrow \quad \text{See the note overleaf.}$$

and $$I_A = I_G + M(AG)^2$$

$\Rightarrow$ $$I_A = I_B - M(BG)^2 + M(AG)^2$$

$\Rightarrow$ $$I_A = I_B + M(AG^2 - BG^2)$$

$$= 0.1807 + 0.9(0.3795)$$

$$= 0.5222$$

The moment of inertia about the end, A, is about 0.52 kg m^2.

The moment of inertia of a rotating body

 The parallel axes theorem

Part **(iv)** of Example 3.11 illustrates the necessity for one of the axes to be through the centre of mass, G, when using the parallel axes theorem. In general, the moments of inertia about parallel axes through two points A and B where AG and BG are perpendicular to the axes are related by the equation

$$I_A = I_B + M(\text{AG}^2 - \text{BG}^2)$$

(Note also that $\text{AG}^2 - \text{BG}^2 \neq \text{AB}^2$.) The moment of inertia of the bat about the player's elbow or shoulder (assuming the arm and wrist are kept rigid) can be calculated using this result.

EXERCISE 3D

1 The following objects have variable density. For each one, find in terms of the given constants (a, k, h, p, q, r)

(i) its mass

(ii) the position of its centre of mass relative to O

(iii) its moment of inertia about the given axis.

Object	Density	Axis
Rod OA of length a	$2x$	Through O perpendicular to rod
Disc centre O, radius a	kr	Through O perpendicular to disc
Rod OA of length a	$p + qx$	Through O perpendicular to rod
Thin cylindrical pipe, height h, base centre O, radius r	$k(h + y)$	y axis

2 A solid circular cylinder of radius a and height h is formed by pouring a resin into a mould and allowing it to set. The resin settles unevenly so that the density of the resulting cylinder is 3ρ at the base and decreases uniformly to ρ at the top.

(i) Write the density as a function of the distance from the base.

(ii) Find the mass, M, of the cylinder.

(iii) Find the position of the centre of mass of the cylinder.

(iv) Find the moment of inertia of the cylinder about its axis of symmetry.

[MEI]

3 (i) Prove, by integration, that the moment of inertia of a thin uniform rod of mass M and length $2a$ about an axis through the centre of the rod and perpendicular to the rod is $\frac{1}{3}Ma^2$.

(ii) Three uniform rods AB, BC and AC have lengths $8a$, $6a$ and $10a$, respectively. Each rod has mass m per unit length. The rods are fastened together to make a triangular frame ABC. Show that the moment of inertia of the frame about a fixed smooth horizontal axis, passing through A and perpendicular to the frame, is $960ma^3$.

(iii) The frame is released from rest with AB horizontal and C vertically above B. Show that when AB is vertical, the angular speed of the frame

is $\sqrt{\dfrac{7g}{20a}}$.

(iv) State which point of the frame has the greatest speed at the instant when AB is vertical, and find this speed in terms of a and g.

[Cambridge]

4 A uniform rod AB, of mass $2m$ and length $2l$, is rigidly attached to a uniform rod BC, of mass m and length l, in such a way that angle ABC is a right angle. Show that the moment of inertia of the frame ABC about an axis through B perpendicular to the plane of the frame is $3ml^2$.

The frame can rotate freely about a fixed, smooth, horizontal axis through B and perpendicular to the plane of the frame. The frame is released from rest in the position in which AB is horizontal and C is below B. At time t, AB makes an angle θ with the horizontal.

(i) Show that

$$l\dot{\theta}^2 = \tfrac{1}{3}g(4\sin\theta + \cos\theta - 1),$$

(ii) Find, in terms of g and l.

(a) the greatest value of $\dot{\theta}^2$.

(b) the greatest speed of A.

[Cambridge]

5 A uniform solid sphere of mass $5m$ and radius a is fixed to the end of a thin uniform rod of mass $3m$ and length $4a$ so that the centre of the sphere lies on the extended axis of the rod. The other end of the rod is freely pivoted at a point in such a way that the system can swing in a vertical plane under the influence of a vertical gravitational field g.

   (i)   Find the moment of inertia of the system about its pivot.

   (ii) If the system is balanced vertically above the pivot and given a slight displacement, find its angular speed at its lowest point.

[MEI]

6 (i) A uniform circular disc of radius a and thickness b has a mass m. Derive an expression for the moment of inertia of this disc about an axis through its centre and perpendicular to its plane.

   (ii) A flywheel is to be made with a radius of 25 cm, a thickness of 5 cm and a moment of inertia about its axis of 1.8 kg m^2. The flywheel is to be constructed with a central disc made from an aluminium alloy, density 2800 kg m^{-3}, and an outer rim of steel, density 7900 kg m^{-3}. Find the radius at which the junction between the central alloy disc and the steel rim must occur.

[MEI]

7 As part of an investigation into rotating interstellar dust clouds a simple mathematical model of such a cloud is proposed. The cloud is assumed to have a uniform density ρ and a shape defined by the volume produced by rotating the area between the curves

$$y = \pm b e^{-\left(\frac{x}{a}\right)^2}, \quad -\infty < x < \infty,$$

about the y axis.

   (i)   Sketch the above curves and shade in the appropriate area.

   (ii) By considering thin cylindrical shells of radius x and thickness δx about the y axis, find an expression for the mass M of the dust cloud in terms of ρ, a and b.

   (iii) Find an expression for the moment of inertia I of the cloud about its axis of symmetry in terms of M and a.

[MEI]

8 (You are given that the moment of inertia about a diameter of a hollow sphere of mass m and radius b is $\frac{2}{3}mb^2$.)

A solid sphere of radius a and mass M has density ρ which varies with radius r

according to the formula $\rho = \rho_0 \left(1 - \frac{r^3}{a^3} \right)$, where ρ_0 is a constant.

(i) Show that $M = \frac{2}{3}\pi\rho_0 a^3$.

(ii) Find the moment of inertia of the sphere about a diameter in terms of M and a.

A uniform hoop has radius a and mass m.

(iii) Assuming that the moment of inertia of this hoop about the axis perpendicular to its plane through its centre is ma^2, deduce its moment of inertia about any diameter.

When the hoop is rotated about a diameter with angular speed ω, its kinetic energy is E. When the sphere is rotated about a diameter with angular velocity 2ω, its kinetic energy is $3E$. Find m in terms of M.

[MEI]

KEY POINTS

1 The moment of inertia of a body about an axis is $I = \sum Mr^2$ and depends on the position and direction of the axis, which should always be stated.

2 Perpendicular axes theorem: $I_z = I_x + I_y$ for a lamina only.

3 Parallel axes theorem:

$$I_A = I_G + Md^2$$
$$= I_G + M(AG)^2 \text{ for AG perpendicular to the axes}$$

4 To find a moment of inertia by integration follow these steps.

- Divide the body into elements for which the moment of inertia is known.
- Find the mass of a typical element in terms of the density.
- Determine the moment of inertia of the element about the axis.
- Sum for all elements and write the sum as an integral.
- Evaluate the integral.
- Write the density in terms of the total mass and replace it.

5 When the density varies, it should be written in terms of a suitable variable and included in the integration.

6 The angular speed of a rigid body about an axis is $\dot{\theta}$, where θ is the angle between a fixed line in the body and a fixed direction in space (both perpendicular to the axis of rotation).

7 The kinetic energy of a body rotating about a fixed axis with angular speed $\dot{\theta}$ and moment of inertia I is $\frac{1}{2}I\dot{\theta}^2$ (or $\frac{1}{2}I\omega^2$).

4 The dynamics of a rotating body

Mechanics is the paradise of the mathematical sciences, because by means of it one comes to the fruits of mathematics.

Leonardo da Vinci, 1452–1519

? An ice-skater might stretch out her arms or draw them in to change her speed of rotation. How does this work?

In Chapter 3 you learnt about the moment of inertia of a rigid body and how to use this to find the kinetic energy of the body as it rotates about a fixed axis. In this chapter you will learn more about fixed-axis rotation, starting from the equation of motion.

The equation of motion for the rotation of a rigid body about a fixed axis

In Chapter 3 the expression for the kinetic energy of a wheel was obtained by summing the energies of individual particles. The same approach is useful for finding the equation of motion for the rotation of a rigid body about a fixed axis. This is the equivalent of Newton's second law for the linear motion of a particle, so first consider the equation of motion for a typical particle in the body. When the rigid body rotates about a fixed axis, each particle in the body moves in a plane in a circle with its centre on the axis, as shown in figure 4.1. Because the body is rigid and rotates about a fixed axis, all the particles in the body have the same angular velocity $\dot{\theta}$ at all times, so they also have the same angular acceleration $\ddot{\theta}$.

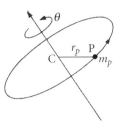

Figure 4.1

A typical particle P rotates in a circle of radius r_p about a point C on the axis. Its acceleration has radial and transverse components $-r_p\dot{\theta}^2$ and $r_p\ddot{\theta}$. These are shown in figure 4.2, together with the resultant force $\mathbf{F}_p$ which acts on the particle in the plane of the motion and is at an angle α to PC.

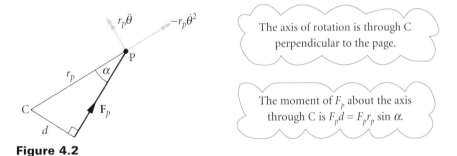

The axis of rotation is through C perpendicular to the page.

The moment of F_p about the axis through C is $F_p d = F_p r_p \sin \alpha$.

Figure 4.2

Newton's second law in the transverse direction (i.e. for circular motion, the tangential direction) gives

$$F_p \sin \alpha = m_p r_p \ddot{\theta}.$$

Multiplying by r_p gives

$$F_p r_p \sin \alpha = m_p r_p^2 \ddot{\theta}.$$

The equation of motion for the rotation of the whole rigid body can be found by summing both sides for all the particles.

$F_p r_p \sin \alpha$ is the moment of the force $\mathbf{F}_p$ about the axis of rotation. This is made up of components which include internal forces as well as the external forces on the body which happen to act on the particular particle.

By Newton's third law, the internal forces are equal and opposite. It is therefore to be expected that, when all the moments of all the forces are summed for all particles, the moments of the internal forces cancel and only the moments of the external forces remain.

Summing both sides of the equation for all particles therefore gives

$$\sum (\text{moments of external forces}) = \sum (m_p r_p^2 \ddot{\theta})$$

$$\left(\sum m_p r_p^2 \right) \ddot{\theta} = I\ddot{\theta}$$

> $\ddot{\theta}$ is the same for all particles

where $I = \sum m_p r_p^2$ as before.

There is no standard notation for a moment and M cannot be used because M is used for mass. In this book C is used to represent the moment of a force about a particular axis (sometimes called a torque) or the moment of a couple. So when the total moment of all forces about the axis is C, the equation of motion for rotation becomes $C = I\ddot{\theta}$.

This is the equivalent of Newton's second law for the rotation of a rigid body about a fixed axis. It is a very concise equation, and the beauty of it is that it can be compared with the equation $F = m\ddot{x}$ for the linear motion of a particle in a similar way to the analogy between kinetic energies met on page 78.

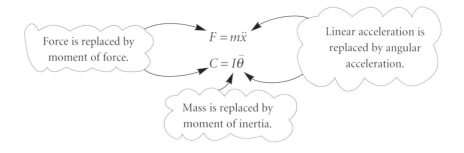

> Force is replaced by moment of force.

$$F = m\ddot{x}$$

$$C = I\ddot{\theta}$$

> Linear acceleration is replaced by angular acceleration.

> Mass is replaced by moment of inertia.

⚠ When using $F = m\ddot{x}$ for linear motion, it is important to take the positive direction of F in the direction of x increasing. In a similar way, moments can be clockwise or anticlockwise and when you use the equation $C = I\ddot{\theta}$, it is important to remember that the moments of the forces should be positive in the same sense as that of increasing θ.

Remember that, although the moment of inertia of a body about an axis is a scalar quantity, its value depends on the position and direction of the axis and this should always be stated.

Wheels in machines

If you visit a place where old machines are conserved, you will see that they often have a large wheel, called a 'flywheel', as part of the driving mechanism. The next example demonstrates why these large wheels are useful.

Two wheels have the same mass M. One can be modelled by a large hollow cylinder of radius R and the other by a smaller solid cylinder of radius r. When they are rotating, they are each subject to a frictional couple of constant magnitude C. While the wheels are being driven, there is a break in power which lasts for a time t. Assuming all units are compatible, find expressions for

(i) the angular retardation of each wheel while the power is off
(ii) the reduction in the angular velocity of each wheel during this time.

The wheels have the same initial angular velocity, and the radius of the larger is twice that of the smaller.

(iii) Show that the percentage reduction in the angular velocity during the time the power is off is eight times greater for the smaller wheel.

(iv) When the wheels are rotating with the same angular speed, show that the kinetic energy of the larger is eight times that of the smaller.

SOLUTION

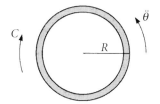
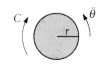

Figure 4.3

(i) When a wheel has an angular acceleration $\ddot{\theta}$ as a result of the action of a couple, $-C$, the equation of motion gives

$$-C = I\ddot{\theta}$$

$$\Rightarrow \qquad \ddot{\theta} = \frac{-C}{I}.$$

The moment of inertia of the hollow cylinder about its axis is MR^2.

Its acceleration is $\dfrac{-C}{MR^2}$.

The moment of inertia of the solid cylinder about its axis is $\frac{1}{2}Mr^2$.

Its acceleration is $\dfrac{-2C}{Mr^2}$.

(ii) For constant angular acceleration α, the new angular velocity, ω, of a wheel after t seconds is

$$\omega = \omega_0 + \alpha t.$$

So the reduction in the angular speed is

$$\omega_0 - \omega = \frac{Ct}{I}.$$

$$\left(\alpha = \frac{-C}{I} \right)$$

The reductions in the angular speeds of the wheels are

$$\frac{Ct}{MR^2} \quad \text{and} \quad \frac{2Ct}{Mr^2}.$$

(iii) When the initial angular speeds are the same, the percentage reductions in the angular speeds are proportional to the actual reductions.

These are in the ratio (larger : smaller) of

$$\frac{Ct}{MR^2} : \frac{2Ct}{Mr^2}$$
$$= r^2 : 2R^2$$
$$= r^2 : 2 \times 4r^2 \quad (R = 2r)$$
$$= 1 : 8.$$

The angular speed is reduced for both wheels, but the percentage reduction is 8 times greater for the smaller wheel.

(iv) When it rotates with angular speed ω, the kinetic energy of a wheel is $\frac{1}{2}I\omega^2$. The ratio of the kinetic energy of the larger wheel to that of the smaller is

$$\frac{1}{2}(MR^2)\omega^2 : \frac{1}{2}(\frac{1}{2}Mr^2)\omega^2$$
$$= R^2 : \frac{1}{2}r^2$$
$$= 4r^2 : \frac{1}{2}r^2$$
$$= 8 : 1$$

The solution to part (iii) of Example 4.1 shows that the use of the larger wheel in the driving mechanism leads to a smaller change in angular speed and so enables the machine to keep working at a steadier rate when there are fluctuations in the power. Such fluctuations are inevitable for many machines. An example is the engine of a car which incorporates a relatively large flywheel, to help smooth out the effects of the intermittent firing in the cylinders. The answer to part (iv) of the example shows, however, that the amount of energy required to set the larger wheel spinning is much greater than that required to make the smaller wheel spin with the same angular speed. This could be a disadvantage and it is also likely to take longer because the angular acceleration is less for the same torque. When the time required to set a wheel in motion is at a premium, as in the case of a racing car, the flywheel is lighter.

When there is surplus energy in a system, flywheels can be used to store energy. There is a bus design which incorporates a flywheel that is activated when braking takes place. When the bus stops some of its energy is stored in the flywheel and this can be used to boost the power of the engine when the bus starts again. Some toys are designed with flywheels to enable them to go on moving much further by themselves after a child stops pushing.

The work done by the moment of a force

When a rigid body rotates about its axis through a small angle $\delta\theta$, the point of application of a typical force F moves through an arc of length $r\delta\theta$, as shown in figure 4.4.

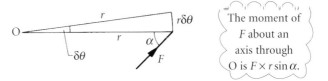

The moment of F about an axis through O is $F \times r\sin\alpha$.

Figure 4.4

The work done by the force is then approximately

$$F\sin\alpha \times r\delta\theta = (F \times r\sin\alpha)\,\delta\theta.$$

This can also be written as (moment about axis) $\times \delta\theta$.

The total work done by this force when the body rotates through an angle θ is thus $\sum \text{moment} \times \delta\theta$.

In the limit as $\delta\theta \to 0$, this becomes $\int (\text{moment})\,d\theta$.

Summing for all the forces, the work done by the total moment, C, is $\int C\,d\theta$.

This again demonstrates the equivalence between the equations for rotation and those for linear motion. It is comparable to $\int F\,dx$ with F replaced by C and x by θ.

When the equation $C = I\ddot{\theta}$ is integrated with respect to θ it gives

$$\int C\,d\theta = \int I\ddot{\theta}\,d\theta$$

$$= I\int \ddot{\theta}\frac{d\theta}{dt}\,dt$$

$$= I\int \ddot{\theta}\dot{\theta}\,dt.$$

But

$$\ddot{\theta}\dot{\theta} = \dot{\theta}\ddot{\theta} = \dot{\theta}\frac{d\dot{\theta}}{dt} = \frac{d}{dt}\left(\tfrac{1}{2}\dot{\theta}^2\right)$$

Compare $v\dfrac{dv}{dt} = \dfrac{d}{dt}\left(\tfrac{1}{2}v^2\right)$

$$\Rightarrow \qquad \int \ddot{\theta}\dot{\theta}\,dt = \tfrac{1}{2}\dot{\theta}^2$$

where the brackets mean 'change in'.

$$\text{and} \qquad \int C\,d\theta = \left[\tfrac{1}{2}I\dot{\theta}^2\right]$$

This is the work–energy equation for a body rotating about a fixed axis.

Note

This equation has been obtained by integrating the equation of motion. Conversely, the energy equation can be differentiated with respect to *t* to give the equation of motion. This is done for the compound pendulum on page 132.

Potential energy change during rotation

The next example illustrates how the use of $\int C \, d\theta$ to find the work done by gravity leads to the expression for the loss in potential energy of the rotating body. The work–energy equation then becomes the equation for the conservation of mechanical energy of the body.

EXAMPLE 4.2

A rigid body of mass M is free to rotate about a horizontal axis through a point A at a distance l from its centre of mass G. Its moment of inertia about the axis is I. The body is displaced through an angle α and let go.

(i) Find, by using $\int C \, d\theta$, the work done by gravity when AG falls into the vertical position and show that this is equal to the loss in potential energy of a particle with the same mass which falls through the same height as G.

(ii) Find an expression for the angular speed when AG is vertical.

SOLUTION

(i) The weight is the force which makes the body rotate about the axis. When it is in the position shown in figure 4.5, the moment of the weight about the axis in the direction of increasing θ is $- Mgl \sin \theta$.

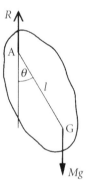

Figure 4.5

The work done by gravity when θ decreases from α to zero is therefore

$$\int_{\alpha}^{0} -Mgl \sin \theta \, d\theta = \Big[Mgl \cos \theta \Big]_{\alpha}^{0}$$

$$= Mgl(1 - \cos \alpha).$$

But the height fallen by G is $h = l(1 - \cos \alpha)$, see figure 4.6. Hence the work done by gravity is equal to Mgh, the loss in potential energy of a particle of mass M which has fallen the same height as G.

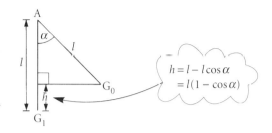

Figure 4.6

(ii) By the work–energy equation, or the principle of conservation of energy, the kinetic energy gained when AG is vertical is given by

$$\tfrac{1}{2}I\dot{\theta}^2 = Mgh.$$

The angular speed at this point is then

$$\sqrt{\frac{2Mgh}{I}} = \sqrt{\frac{2Mgl}{I}(1-\cos\alpha)}$$

Note

The assumption that the potential energy of a large body is the same as that of a particle of equal mass situated at G follows from the definition of G. If Oy is the co-ordinate axis in the vertical direction, then

$$M\bar{y} = \sum (m_p y_p) \quad \Rightarrow \quad Mg\bar{y} = \sum (m_p g y_p).$$

A winch is a useful device for applying a force to a moving object. For example, winches are used for towing gliders into the air and as lifting devices on boats. The photograph below shows a cylinder with a rope wrapped round it, which is used to raise bags of flour in an old working mill.

The well bucket in the next example is raised and lowered using a similar device.

EXAMPLE 4.3

A bucket of mass m for drawing water from a well is attached by a light rope to a cylinder of mass M and radius r. The rope is wound round the cylinder using a light handle and the bucket is then allowed to fall freely from rest. What is its speed when it has fallen a height h

(i) when there is no resistance to its motion

(ii) when there is a constant resistive couple of magnitude C?

SOLUTION

(i) Consider the energy of the cylinder and the bucket and let the zero level of potential energy be the initial position of the bucket. The tension T in the rope does no work because it is an internal force.

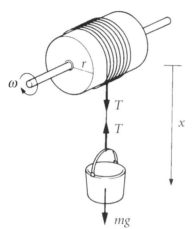

Note that the axle exerts an upwards force on the cylinder which balances T and the weight of the cylinder. These forces together form a *couple*; the effect is purely rotational.

Figure 4.7

Suppose the speed of the bucket is v when the angular speed of the cylinder is ω. While the cylinder rotates through an angle θ, the bucket falls a height x where

$$x = r\theta$$

Differentiating $\Rightarrow$ $v = r\omega$

After falling a height h from rest, the total energy of the bucket is $\frac{1}{2}mv^2 - mgh$.

The cylinder also has a kinetic energy due to its rotation of

$$\frac{1}{2}I\omega^2 = \frac{1}{2}(\frac{1}{2}Mr^2)\omega^2$$
$$= \frac{1}{4}Mr^2\omega^2.$$

So the total energy of the bucket and cylinder when the bucket has fallen a height h is

$$\frac{1}{4}Mv^2 + \frac{1}{2}mv^2 - mgh.$$

The initial energy is zero so, by the principle of conservation of energy,

$$\frac{1}{4}Mv^2 + \frac{1}{2}mv^2 - mgh = 0$$

$$\Rightarrow \qquad \frac{1}{4}(M+2m)v^2 = mgh$$

$$\Rightarrow \qquad v^2 = \frac{4mgh}{2m+M}$$

$$\Rightarrow \qquad v = \sqrt{\frac{4mgh}{2m+M}}$$

(ii) When there is a resistive couple C, the work done against the couple is

$$\int C\, d\theta = C\theta$$

$$= \frac{Ch}{r} \qquad (x = h = r\theta)$$

Then the gain in kinetic energy is the difference between the work done by gravity and the work done against the resistance

$$\Rightarrow \qquad \frac{1}{2}mv^2 + \frac{1}{4}Mv^2 = mgh - \frac{Ch}{r}$$

$$\Rightarrow \qquad \frac{1}{4}(2m+M)v^2 = \frac{(mgrh - Ch)}{r}$$

$$\Rightarrow \qquad v^2 = \frac{4(mgr - C)h}{(2m+M)r}$$

$$\Rightarrow \qquad v = \sqrt{\frac{4(mgr - C)h}{(2m+M)r}}.$$

INVESTIGATION

The rope on the winch illustrated on page 123 probably has a density of the same order as the wooden cylinder and is clearly not of negligible thickness. Given that the diameter of the winch is about 0.3 m and the density of wood is about 600 kg m^{-3}, use measurements on the picture to estimate the velocity acquired by a bag of flour of mass 8 kg if it falls through a height of 10 m while attached to the end of the rope. You might decide to ignore resistances to motion, but do not ignore the rope.

The next example illustrates the use of the work–energy principle when the moment of a force about the axis is not constant.

EXAMPLE 4.4

A shed door of mass 30 kg, width 0.76 m and height 1.8 m is standing open at 90° when a gust of wind hits it. The wind is initially perpendicular to the door and does not change its direction as the door shuts. The resultant force on the door due to the wind acts through its centre and is of magnitude 10 N per m² of door 'facing' the wind. A constant frictional couple of 2 Nm opposes the motion of the door.

(i)   Assuming the door is a lamina, find its moment of inertia about its axis of rotation.

(ii) Find the moment of the force of the wind about the hinges when the door is open at an angle θ.

(iii) Use the work–energy principle to find the angular speed of the door when it shuts.

SOLUTION

(i)   The moment of inertia is given by $\frac{4}{3}Ml^2$. In this case

$$2l = 0.76$$

$$\Rightarrow \qquad l = 0.38$$

$$\Rightarrow \qquad \text{moment of inertia} = \frac{4}{3} \times 30 \times (0.38)^2 \text{ kg m}^2$$

$$= 5.776 \text{ kg m}^2.$$

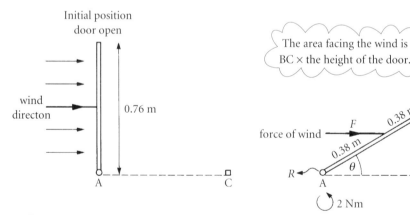

Figure 4.8

(ii) When the door is open at an angle θ, the area facing the wind is

$$0.76 \sin \theta \times 1.8 = 1.368 \sin \theta \, \text{m}^2.$$

The force due to the wind is then $13.68 \sin \theta$ N. It acts through the centre, so its moment about the axis of rotation is

$$13.68 \sin \theta \times 0.38 \sin \theta = 5.1984 \sin^2 \theta \, \text{Nm}.$$

(iii) There is a frictional couple of 2 Nm resisting the motion, so the resultant moment in the direction of increasing θ is $-(5.1984 \sin^2 \theta - 2)$Nm.

The work in joules done in turning the door from $\theta = \dfrac{\pi}{2}$ radians to $\theta = 0$ is

$$\int_{\frac{\pi}{2}}^{0} -(5.1984 \sin^2 \theta - 2)\mathrm{d}\theta - \int_{0}^{\frac{\pi}{2}} + (5.1984 \sin^2 \theta - 2)\mathrm{d}\theta$$

$$= \int_{0}^{\frac{\pi}{2}} (5.1984 \times \tfrac{1}{2}(1 - \cos 2\theta) - 2)\mathrm{d}\theta$$

$$= \left[2.5992\theta - 1.2996 \sin 2\theta - 2\theta \right]_{0}^{\frac{\pi}{2}}$$

$$= 0.5992 \times \dfrac{\pi}{2}$$

$$= 0.9412$$

By the work–energy principle, this is equal to the gain in kinetic energy, $\frac{1}{2}I\dot{\theta}^2$.

From part **(i)** the moment of inertia about the axis of rotation is 5.776 kg m².

$$\Rightarrow \qquad 0.9412 = \tfrac{1}{2} \times 5.776 \times \dot{\theta}^2$$

$$\Rightarrow \qquad \dot{\theta}^2 = 0.3259$$

The angular speed is 0.571 rad s⁻¹ (to 3 significant figures).

 Remember angles must be in radians when using calculus.

1 The flywheel of a car can be modelled as a disc of diameter 0.2 m and thickness 0.02 m from which another concentric disc of diameter 0.07 m has been removed. The density of the wheel is 7800 kg m⁻³.

(i) Find its moment of inertia about its axis.

The starter motor of the engine of the car makes the flywheel rotate at 50 rev s⁻¹ in 3 seconds starting from rest. Find

(ii) its angular acceleration (assumed constant)

(iii) the average couple required to accelerate the flywheel

(iv) the kinetic energy of the flywheel after 3 seconds.

2 A garden gate can be modelled as a rectangular lamina of width 0.9 m and mass 20 kg. It is kept shut by a spring mechanism which applies a couple equal to $4(1 + \theta)$ Nm when the gate is opened through an angle of θ radians. The gate is opened 1.5 radians and then allowed to shut naturally.

(i) Find the moment of inertia of the gate about its hinges.

(ii) Find the work done in opening the gate 1.5 radians.

(iii) Assuming there is no loss of energy due to friction, find the angular speed of the gate just before it shuts.

3 A microwave oven has a turntable which can be modelled as a disc of mass 0.9 kg and radius 0.16 m rotating at $\frac{\pi}{6}$ rad s^{-1}.

(i) The turntable has an angular retardation of 0.4 rad s^{-2}. Find the magnitude of the frictional couple acting.

A cylindrical cake of mass 0.6 kg and radius 0.9 m is placed centrally on the turntable and cooked in a light plastic container for 6 minutes at a power of 650 W.

(ii) Assuming the same constant frictional couple, find .
    (a) the kinetic energy, A, given to the cake and turntable
    (b) the work done, B, in keeping the turntable rotating at $\frac{\pi}{6}M$ rad s^{-1}
    (c) the energy, C, required to cook the cake.
(iii) What is the ratio of the energies $A : B : C$?

4 The front wheel of a bicycle is rotating freely at 20 rad s^{-1} when the brakes are applied. The wheel, which can be modelled as a hoop of mass 2 kg and radius 0.3 m, is brought to rest in 0.08 seconds by two brake blocks applied to its rim. Find

(i) the angular deceleration of the wheel (assumed constant)
(ii) the angle turned through before coming to rest
(iii) the total frictional force applied by the brake blocks
(iv) the total contact force between the blocks and the wheel, given that the coefficient of friction is 0.9.

When the wheel is wet the coefficient of friction is reduced to 0.3.

(v) Assuming the same contact force, find the angle turned through while the wheel comes to rest in this case.

5 Chris wishes to find the resistance to the motion of a bicycle and decides to start by investigating the resistance to the front wheel. When an object of mass 50 g is placed on the valve it turns from rest in position A through 160° before coming to rest at B. OA is horizontal.

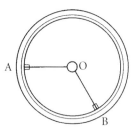

(i) Assuming the valve has a mass of 10 g and is 28.5 cm from the centre of the wheel, find the loss in potential energy between A and B.
(ii) Show that the resistive couple is about 0.0205 Nm.

When Chris flicks the wheel into motion (without the object), it comes to rest in 41 seconds after making 28 revolutions.

(iii) Find the angular retardation (assumed constant) of the wheel, and its moment of inertia about its axle given the same resistive couple.

(iv) The wheel has a mass of 2 kg and its radius is 30 cm. Find the moment of inertia of a hoop with these measurements.

Comment on these results.

6 A uniform rectangular shop sign ABCD has mass 1.8 kg and sides AB = 0.4 m and BC = 0.3 m. The sign is hung along the edge AB, which is horizontal, and is free to rotate about this edge.

(i) Calculate the moment of inertia of the sign about AB.

(ii) Assuming that there are no forces acting other than gravity, and that $g = 10$ ms^{-2}, show that, when the sign makes a small angle θ with the vertical, $\ddot{\theta} \approx -50\theta$.

(iii) Hence find the period of small oscillations of the shop sign.

7 A toy engine of total mass 75 g contains a uniform flywheel of mass 15 g and radius 1.2 cm. The wheels of the engine are of radius 1 cm and they are attached to the flywheel with gears which ensure that the flywheel rotates 20 times as fast as they do. The engine is pushed 4 cm along the floor with a force of 20 N and let go.

(i) Find the angular speed of the flywheel when the speed of the engine is v ms^{-1}.

(ii) Assuming that the kinetic energy of the toy consists only of the rotational energy of the flywheel and the linear energy of the whole engine, find the speed of the engine when it is released.

8 A pulley wheel is a disc of mass M and radius a, and can turn freely about a horizontal axis through its centre. Particles of mass M and $\frac{1}{2}M$ hang vertically over the pulley at the ends of a rough, light string. When the system is set in motion, the string does not slip over the pulley.

(i) By considering the equations of motion of the pulley and the two particles, show that the acceleration of the particles is $\frac{1}{4}g$.

(ii) Find the difference in tension between the two portions of the string.

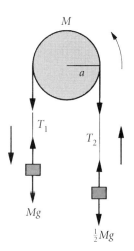

The compound pendulum

A compound pendulum is any rigid body which oscillates freely about a fixed horizontal axis. No external forces or couples act on the pendulum apart from its weight and a supporting force at the axis. The next example shows that such a pendulum performs approximate simple harmonic motion when the oscillations are small.

EXAMPLE 4.5

A compound pendulum, of mass M and centre of mass G, is free to rotate about a fixed horizontal axis through a point A. AG is perpendicular to the axis of rotation and of length h. The moments of inertia of the pendulum about the fixed axis and a parallel axis through G are I_A and I_G respectively. Find expressions for

(i) the period of small oscillations of the pendulum

(ii) the length of a simple pendulum with the same period (called the *simple equivalent pendulum*)

(iii) the period in terms of the radius of gyration, k, of the pendulum about the axis through G.

When such a pendulum has a period of 2 seconds, it is called a *seconds pendulum*.

(iv) Show that, for a seconds pendulum, k cannot be greater than about $\frac{1}{2}$.

(v) Find the value of h for which the period is a minimum.

SOLUTION

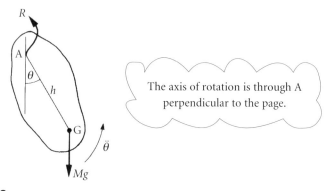

The axis of rotation is through A perpendicular to the page.

Figure 4.9

(i) When AG makes an angle θ with the downward vertical as shown, taking moments about the axis gives

$$Mg \sin \theta \times h = I_A (-\ddot{\theta})$$

$\ddot{\theta} > 0$ in the direction of increasing θ

where I_A is the moment of inertia about the fixed axis.

$$\Rightarrow \qquad \ddot{\theta} = -\frac{Mgh}{I_A} \sin \theta$$

Hence, for small θ, $\ddot{\theta} = -\dfrac{Mgh}{I_A}\theta$.

This represents simple harmonic motion with period $T = 2\pi\sqrt{\dfrac{I_A}{Mgh}}$.   ①

By the parallel axes theorem $I_A = I_G + Mh^2$. Therefore, the period for small

oscillations is $T = 2\pi\sqrt{\dfrac{I_G + Mh^2}{Mgh}}$.

(ii) The period for small oscillations of a simple pendulum of length l is

$2\pi\sqrt{\dfrac{l}{g}}$ so the length of an equivalent simple pendulum is

$$l = \frac{I_G + Mh^2}{Mh} \quad \text{or} \quad l = \frac{I_A}{Mh} \quad \text{(from ①)}$$

(iii) The radius of gyration about the axis through G is k, so

$$I_G = Mk^2 \quad \Rightarrow \quad I_A = Mk^2 + Mh^2.$$

The period is then

$$T = 2\pi\sqrt{\frac{M(k^2 + h^2)}{Mgh}} \quad \text{(from ①)}$$

$$\Rightarrow \qquad T = 2\pi\sqrt{\frac{k^2 + h^2}{gh}}. \qquad\qquad ②$$

(iv) For a given pendulum the length h, and hence the position of A, can usually be calculated so that it has the correct period. A seconds pendulum has a period of 2 seconds.

In this case, $T = 2$ and squaring both sides of ② gives

$$4 = 4\pi^2 \frac{(k^2 + h^2)}{gh}$$

$$\Rightarrow \qquad gh = \pi^2(k^2 + h^2)$$

$$\Rightarrow \qquad h^2 - \left(\frac{g}{\pi^2}\right)h + k^2 = 0$$

This has real roots for h provided $\left(\dfrac{g}{\pi^2}\right)^2 \geqslant 4k^2$.

$$\Rightarrow \qquad k \leqslant \frac{1}{2}\left(\frac{g}{\pi^2}\right)$$

But $\dfrac{g}{\pi^2} = 0.994 \approx 1$, so k cannot be greater than about $\frac{1}{2}$.

(v) Consider the function

$$f(h) = \frac{(k^2 + h^2)}{h} = \frac{k^2}{h} + h.$$

The period is least when f(h) is a minimum. Differentiating gives

$$f'(h) = -k^2 h^{-2} + 1$$

so the minimum occurs when $k^2 = h^2$, that is $h = k$.

The period is least when AG is equal to the radius of gyration about the axis through G. (You can check that $f''(k) > 0$ to ensure a *minimum*.)

Deriving the compound pendulum equation using energy methods

It is sometimes easier to derive the equation of motion by differentiating the energy equation. This can be done in the compound pendulum problem as follows.

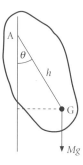

Figure 4.10

The kinetic energy is given by $\frac{1}{2} I_A \dot{\theta}^2$.

Taking A as the base level, the potential energy when the centre of mass is at the position shown in figure 4.10 is

$$-Mgh \cos \theta.$$

The total energy is constant so that

$$\tfrac{1}{2} I_A \dot{\theta}^2 - Mgh \cos \theta = \text{constant.}$$

Differentiating with respect to time gives

$$I_A \dot{\theta} \ddot{\theta} + Mgh \sin \theta \dot{\theta} = 0.$$

Note that $\dfrac{d}{dt} \dot{\theta}^2 = 2\dot{\theta} \dfrac{d\dot{\theta}}{dt}$.

Dividing by $\dot{\theta}$ and rearranging gives

$$\ddot{\theta} = -\frac{Mgh}{I_A}\sin\theta$$

as derived previously.

A similar method is used in Chapter 5 to find the period of small oscillations about a position of stable equilibrium.

INVESTIGATION

How long does a clock pendulum need to be? (Or why are grandfather clocks too tall for the shelf?)

A pendulum which oscillates with a period of 2 seconds is called a seconds pendulum (the clock ticks every half period). Investigate the dimensions of a seconds pendulum in the following cases. You will find it helpful to use the approximation $\pi^2 = g$.

(i)   A simple pendulum with a bob.

(ii) A disc of radius r attached to a light rod so that the centre of the disc is a distance d from the axis of rotation.

     What is r if $d = r$? Find d in terms of r in other cases.

(iii) A rod pivoted about a point at a distance d from its centre. (d must be real and the pivot must be on the rod).

Investigate the periods of other types of clock pendulum.

The angular momentum of a rigid body rotating about a fixed axis

When Newton's first two laws are written in terms of the linear momentum of a particle they are equivalent to the following two statements.

● The linear momentum of a particle is constant if no resultant force acts on it.
● The resultant force acting on the particle is equal to the rate of change of its linear momentum.

But how do these laws apply to rotating rigid bodies? Think, for example, of the motion of a rotating space station which has escaped from all external forces. The direction of motion of each particle is continually changing but this does not mean that Newton's laws are contradicted. Although external forces are non-existent, all the particles in the station have forces acting upon them due to their interaction with each other. These internal forces are essential for parts of the space station to retain their rigid shape.

The momentum of a particle is a vector and so it is possible to find its *moment* about the axis of rotation. This moment of momentum is called the *angular momentum of the particle about the axis*. When a rigid body rotates about a fixed axis and the external forces have no resultant moment about the axis, the total angular momentum about the axis is constant. This is shown below.

Figure 4.11 shows a typical particle P of mass m_p rotating with angular speed $\dot{\theta}_p$ in a circle of radius r_p about a fixed axis. Its momentum is $m_p v_p = m_p r_p \dot{\theta}_p$ along the tangent so the moment of its momentum about the axis is

$$(m_p v_p) r_p = m_p r_p^2 \dot{\theta}_p.$$

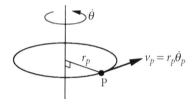

Figure 4.11

Summing for all particles gives the total angular momentum, L, about the axis, namely

$$L = \sum_{\text{all } p} m_p r_p^2 \dot{\theta}_p.$$

For a rigid body, all the particles have the same angular speed, $\dot{\theta}$, about the axis, so the expression for angular momentum becomes

$$L = I\dot{\theta}$$

where $I = \sum m_p r_p^2$ is the moment of inertia of the body about the axis. This expression for angular momentum is analogous to mv for linear motion, as you might expect.

When a rigid body rotates about a fixed axis, the conservation of angular momentum in the absence of external forces follows from the equation of motion

$$C = I\ddot{\theta}$$

where C is the total moment of forces about the axis. When there are no external forces $C = 0$,

$$\Rightarrow \qquad I\ddot{\theta} = 0$$

$$\Rightarrow \qquad I\dot{\theta} = \text{constant}$$

This is the equivalent of Newton's first law of motion. The second law has already been written in the form $C = I\ddot{\theta}$, but it too can be written in terms of the angular momentum of the body:

$$C = \frac{d}{dt}(I\dot{\theta}) = \frac{dL}{dt}$$

This is an important result which can be stated as follows.

● For a rigid body rotating about a fixed axis the resultant moment of forces about the axis of rotation is equal to the rate of change of angular momentum of the body about the axis.

Conservation of angular momentum

An important principle can be deduced from the previous section.

If there is no resultant moment of external forces acting on a body rotating about a fixed axis, its angular momentum remains constant.

It is conservation of angular momentum which explains why a spinning ice-skater draws in her arms to go faster and why a rotating interstellar gas cloud speeds up if it contracts under gravitational attraction.

EXAMPLE 4.6

A turntable which can be modelled as a disc of radius 0.2 m and mass 5 kg is spinning horizontally about an axis through its centre 3 times a second. An object of mass 2 kg is gently placed on it 0.15 m from the centre and remains in place through friction. How fast does the turntable now rotate?

SOLUTION

The angular momentum of the system as a whole is conserved.

The moment of inertia of the turntable is $\frac{1}{2} \times 5 \times 0.2^2 = 0.1 \, \text{kg m}^2$.

The turntable is rotating at $3 \times 2\pi = 6\pi \, \text{rad s}^{-1}$.

So the initial angular momentum is $0.1 \times 6\pi = 0.6\pi$ (the object is initially at rest).

If the final angular velocity is ω, the angular momentum of the turntable is 0.1ω.

The speed of the object is 0.15ω so its angular momentum about the axis is

$$\text{mass} \times \text{tangential speed} \times \text{distance from axis} = 2 \times 0.15\omega \times 0.15$$
$$= 0.045\omega.$$

Hence the total final angular momentum is 0.145ω.

$$0.145\omega = 0.6\pi$$
$$\Rightarrow \qquad \omega = 4.14\pi \, \text{rad s}^{-1}$$

which is 2.1 rotations per second.

To find the final angular momentum, L, you may prefer to work out the moment of inertia, I, of the turntable plus object and then simply apply $L = I\omega$. This will give the same result.

Note that, although the angular momentum has been conserved, some energy will have been lost. The object was accelerated from rest to its final velocity over a very short period during which some slight movement must have occurred and energy will have been lost overcoming friction.

The impulse of a couple about an axis

Integrating the equation for C gives

$$\int C \, dt = [I\dot{\theta}] = [L]$$

The brackets indicate the change in L: e.g. $I\omega - I\omega_0$.

This is the equivalent of $\int F \, dt = [mv]$ for linear motion. In that case $\int F \, dt$ is called an *impulse*. For rotation $\int C \, dt$ can be regarded as the impulse of a torque or a couple. This gives the following important result.

● The sum of the moments of impulses about the axis of rotation is equal to the change in angular momentum of the body about the same axis.

EXAMPLE 4.7

In a party game a flat board in the shape of a space ship is made to spin round a fixed vertical axis when hit by a small 'meteorite' of mass m. The board is always stationary and facing the player when a meteorite is thrown. Meteorites, which can stick to the board, are not removed between throws. The moment of inertia of the board about its axis is I.

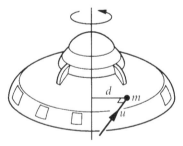

Figure 4.12

(i) Assuming that a meteorite is thrown at the empty board and sticks after hitting it at right angles with speed u at a distance d from the axis, find the initial angular velocity of the board.

(ii) The board slows down under the action of a constant frictional couple C and the winner in the game is the person who makes it spin for the longest time. Is this a fair game?

(iii) Someone suggests that it would be easier to determine the winner by counting the number of revolutions made by the board before coming to rest. Would the game be fair in this case?

SOLUTION

(i) During the short period of time taken by the impact, the impulse of the frictional couple is negligible, so the change in total angular momentum about the axis is negligible. In other words, total angular momentum is conserved. You can compare this with conservation of linear momentum when two objects collide.

The angular momentum of the meteorite about the axis just before it hits the board is $mu \times d$. The new moment of inertia of the meteorite and board about the axis after the collision is $I + md^2$, so the angular momentum after the collision is $(I + md^2)\omega$, where ω is the angular speed. Hence

$$(I + md^2)\omega = mud \quad \Rightarrow \quad \omega = \frac{mud}{(I + md^2)}. \qquad \text{①}$$

(ii) The impulse of the constant frictional couple in time t is Ct and this is equal to the loss of angular momentum of the board and meteorite during that time. When t is the time for the board to stop rotating:

$$Ct = mud \quad \Rightarrow \quad t = \frac{mud}{C}.$$

This depends only on the speed of the meteorite and the position where it hits the board, and is independent of the moment of inertia of the board when it is hit. So it does not matter how many other meteorites are there already. Provided there is sufficient room on the board, the game is fair.

(iii) Suppose that I_n is the moment of inertia of the board about its axis when there are n meteorites attached to it. After another hit this will become $I_n + md^2$. The initial angular speed after this additional meteorite hits the space ship is

$$\omega = \frac{mud}{(I_n + md^2)} \qquad (\text{see ①})$$

When the board has turned through an angle θ, the work done against the couple is $C\theta$ and this is equal to the loss in kinetic energy. Hence

$$C\theta = \tfrac{1}{2}(I_n + md^2)\omega^2 \quad \Rightarrow \quad \theta = \frac{(mud)^2}{2C(I_n + md^2)}.$$

This is dependent on the value of I_n so it will be more difficult to make the board turn through a given angle as the game progresses. In this case, the game is not fair.

1 A thin uniform rod of mass M and length $2a$ performs approximate simple harmonic oscillations about a perpendicular axis through one end.

   (i)   By taking moments about the axis, write down the equation of motion of the rod.
   (ii) Find the period of small oscillations of the rod.
   (iii) Find the length of a simple pendulum with the same period.

2 A clock pendulum consists of a uniform thin rod of length $2l$ and mass m, to the end of which is attached a thin disc of radius l and mass $2m$.

   (i)   Find the moment of inertia of the pendulum about an axis perpendicular to the disc through the free end of the rod.
   (ii) By taking moments about the axis, find the equation of motion and hence the period of small oscillations of the pendulum.
   (iii) Find the value of l if this period is 2 seconds.

3 A cricket bat of mass M kg is pivoted about a horizontal axis through a point A on the handle as shown. The axis is perpendicular to the page, G is the centre of mass and AG = a m.

The period of small oscillations about the axis is found to be T seconds.

Show that the moment of inertia of the bat about the axis is $I_A = \dfrac{MgaT^2}{4\pi^2}$.

In order that there should be no impulsive reaction at A when the ball is hit, the impact must be at the 'sweet spot' B given by $b = \dfrac{aI_G}{I_A - I_G}$. Show that $a + b = \dfrac{gT^2}{4\pi^2}$.

4 A rigid body of mass M and centre of mass G is free to rotate about a horizontal axis through a point A. Its moment of inertia about the axis of rotation is Ma^2, AG is perpendicular to the axis and of length $\dfrac{a}{2}$. When the body is hanging at rest with AG vertical it is hit at G by a horizontal impulse $Ma\omega$ perpendicular to the axis of rotation.

   (i)   By taking moments about the axis, find an expression for the initial angular speed ω_0.
   (ii) Use the principle of conservation of energy to find an expression for $a\dot\theta^2$ when AG has turned through an angle θ.
   (iii) Differentiate your expression for $a\dot\theta^2$ with respect to t to find an expression for $a\ddot\theta$ in the same position.
   (iv) Verify that your answer for $a\ddot\theta$ is the same as you would obtain using the equation of motion for rotation about the axis.

5 A rod AB, of mass m and length $4l$, is free to rotate in a vertical plane about a horizontal axis through a point C at a distance l from A. When it is hanging vertically, the rod is hit at B by a horizontal impulse J which is perpendicular to the axis of rotation.

   (i)   Use the parallel axis theorem to show that the moment of inertia of the rod about the axis is $\frac{7}{3}ml^2$.
   (ii) Find an expression for the initial angular speed of the rod.
   (iii) Use the principle of conservation of energy to find an expression for the least value of J which will cause the rod to make complete revolutions about the axis of rotation.

6 A smooth rod AB, of mass M and length $2a$, has a small ring of mass $\frac{1}{6}M$ threaded on it. The rod is free to turn in a horizontal plane about a vertical axis through A. The ring is held at the mid-point of the rod while it is set in motion with angular speed ω and then released.

   (i)   By considering the forces acting on the ring, explain why it will not stay in its initial position relative to the rod.
   (ii) Find the angular momentum of the rod and the ring at the instant the ring is released.
   (iii) Explain why angular momentum is conserved once the ring is released and show that the angular speed of the rod and the ring when the ring reaches B is $\frac{3}{4}\omega$.

7 Two gear wheels are such that, when they are engaged, their angular speeds are inversely proportional to their radii. One has a radius a and moment of inertia pa^2 about its axis of rotation. The other gear wheel has radius b and moment of inertia qb^2. The first is rotating with angular speed ω when it engages with the second which is initially at rest.

   (i)   By considering the change in angular momentum of each wheel separately, find the impulse between the teeth of the gear wheels when they engage.
   (ii) Find the angular speed of each wheel.
   (iii) Why is the angular momentum not conserved?
   (iv) Find the energy lost when the gears engage.

8 This question describes a simplified model of a device used to de-spin a satellite. A uniform circular disc of mass $12m$ and radius a lies on a smooth horizontal table and is free to rotate about a fixed vertical axis through its centre. A light wire is attached to a point on the rim of the disc and is wound round this rim. A particle of mass m is attached to the free end of the wire and is initially attached to the rim.

When the disc is rotating with angular speed ω in the opposite sense to that in which the wire is wound the particle is released so that the wire unwinds and remains taut. The length of the wire is chosen so that it is completely unwound at the instant that the disc stops rotating. The particle is then moving at right angles to the wire.

Use the principles of conservation of angular momentum and energy to find the length of the wire.

9 A square board, of side $2a$ m and mass M kg, is to be used to estimate the speed of bullets. It is freely hinged about one horizontal edge and hangs at rest in a vertical plane. A bullet of mass m kg travelling horizontally with speed V ms^{-1} hits the board at its centre and becomes embedded in it. The board then rotates through an angle α before coming to rest.

(i) Show that the initial angular speed of the board is $\dfrac{3mV}{(4M+3m)a}$.

(ii) Show also that

$$V^2 = \frac{2ga}{3m^2}(M+m)(4M+3m)(1-\cos\alpha).$$

(iii) Evaluate V when $M = 5$, $m = 0.005$, $a = 0.1$, $\alpha = 0.2$ radians.

10 A uniform rod of mass M and length $2l$ is hinged at one end so that it can rotate freely in a vertical plane. While suspended at rest, the lower end is struck by a bullet, mass m, moving horizontally with velocity v in the same plane. The bullet is embedded in the rod which begins to rotate.

(i) Show that if m is small compared to M, the initial angular velocity of the rod is approximately $\dfrac{3mv}{2Ml}$.

(ii) Hence show the rod undergoes a complete revolution if the initial linear momentum of the bullet is greater than $2M\sqrt{\frac{1}{3}lg}$.

11 (i) Show that the moment of inertia of a uniform rod, of length $2a$ and mass m, about an axis through a point a distance h from its centre of gravity and perpendicular to the plane containing the rod and the point, is $\frac{1}{3}m(a^2 + 3h^2)$.

(ii) A uniform equilateral triangular lamina of side $2l$ has mass M. By considering the lamina as a series of thin rods, determine the moment of inertia of the lamina about an axis through a vertex and perpendicular to its plane.

(iii) (a) The triangle is enlarged by a factor k, with its mass per unit area remaining the same as before. Show that the moment of inertia of the new triangle about an axis through its vertex and perpendicular to its plane is $\frac{5}{3}Mk^4l^2$.

(b) Find the period of small oscillations about the same axis when this lamina is freely suspended, and show that this is proportional to $\sqrt{k}$.

[Oxford]

12 The diagram shows two small uniform hollow spheres of mass $2m$ and radius a and a larger hollow uniform sphere of mass $10m$ and radius $2a$. Each of the smaller spheres is joined to the larger one by a small solid uniform rod of mass m and length $2a$. The line containing the rods passes through the centres of the three spheres.

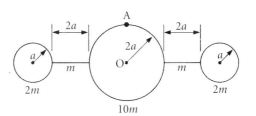

(i) Show that the moment of inertia of the system about an axis through the centre O of the larger sphere and perpendicular to the line containing the rods is $148ma^2$.

(ii) A wire is attached to the highest point A of the larger sphere and the system is suspended in equilibrium from this wire so that the vertical through O is along the wire. The wire is such that when the line containing the rods is turned through a small angle θ about the wire then a restoring couple of magnitude $mk\theta$, where k is a positive constant, is exerted on the system.

Find the period of small oscillations of the system about the vertical axis containing the wire.

[Oxford]

13 A rough uniform rod AB, of mass m and length $2r$, can rotate freely in a vertical plane about a fixed smooth horizontal axis through the point C of the rod, where $AC = \frac{1}{2}r$. A small bead of mass $3m$ can slide on the rod. Initially the rod is held in a horizontal position with the bead at the end A of the rod. The rod is released from rest and after a time t the rod makes an angle θ with the horizontal. For the part of the motion in which the bead remains at rest relative to the rod,

(i) show that $\dot{\theta}^2 = \dfrac{3g\sin\theta}{2r}$

(ii) show that the magnitude of the frictional component of the force of the rod on the bead is $\frac{21}{4}mg\sin\theta$

(iii) differentiate the expression for $\dot{\theta}^2$ with respect to t and hence, or otherwise, show that $\ddot{\theta} = \dfrac{3g}{4r}\cos\theta$

(iv) find the magnitude of the normal component of the force of the rod on the bead.

(v) The coefficient of friction between the bead and the rod is $\frac{4}{5}$. Find, to the nearest degree, the value of θ at the instant when the bead is about to slide off the rod.

[**Cambridge**, *adapted*]

14 A thin uniform rod, of mass m and length $6a$, can rotate freely in a vertical plane about a fixed horizontal axis through one end A of the rod. A uniform circular disc, of mass $12m$ and radius a, is clamped to the rod so that its centre C lies on the rod and its plane coincides with the plane in which the rod can rotate. Given that $AC = x$, find, in terms of m, a and x, expressions for

(i) the distance of the centre of mass of the system from A

(ii) the moment of inertia of the system about the axis of rotation.

(iii) Show that T, the period of small oscillations of the system, is given by
$$T^2 g(a + 4x) = 8\pi^2(3a^2 + 2x^2).$$

(iv) Hence show that the minimum value of T occurs when $x = a$.

[AEB]

15 A uniform square lamina of mass m and side $2a$ is freely pivoted about one corner.

(i) Find the moment of inertia of the lamina about an axis through the pivot and perpendicular to the plane of the lamina.

When the lamina is hanging at rest in a vertical plane an impulse J is applied to it along the horizontal diagonal.

(ii) Find the initial angular speed of the lamina about the pivot in terms of m, a and J.

As a result of the impulse the lamina spins completely about the pivot and its angular speed at the highest point is half that at the lowest point.

(iii) Find J in terms of m, a and g.

[MEI]

Rotation about a fixed axis

1 Angular momentum: $L = I\dot{\theta}$

2 Moment of force about axis: $C = \dfrac{\mathrm{d}L}{\mathrm{d}t} = I\ddot{\theta}$

3 When there is no resultant moment about the axis, angular momentum is conserved.

4 The sum of moments of impulses about an axis is the change in the angular momentum about the same axis.

5 Mechanical energy is conserved if no external forces other than gravity do work.

Equivalent quantities

Rotation of a rigid body about a fixed axis		Linear motion	
● Moment of inertia about axis:	$I = \sum mr^2$	Mass:	m
● Moment of force about axis:	C	Force:	F
● Angular displacement:	θ	Displacement:	x or s
● Angular velocity:	$\dot{\theta}$ or ω	Velocity:	$\dot{x}$ or v
● Angular momentum:	$L = I\dot{\theta}$	Momentum:	$m\dot{x}$
● Equation of motion:	$C = I\ddot{\theta} = \dfrac{\mathrm{d}L}{\mathrm{d}t}$	$F = m\ddot{x} = \dfrac{\mathrm{d}(m\dot{x})}{\mathrm{d}t}$	
● Kinetic energy:	$\frac{1}{2}I\dot{\theta}^2$ or $\frac{1}{2}I\omega^2$	$\frac{1}{2}m\dot{x}^2$ or $\frac{1}{2}mv^2$	
● Work:	$\int C\,\mathrm{d}\theta$	$\int F\,\mathrm{d}x$ or $\int F\,\mathrm{d}s$	
● Impulse:	$\int C\,\mathrm{d}t$	$\int F\,\mathrm{d}t$	

Stability of equilibrium

A government so situated is in the condition called in mechanics
'unstable equilibrium' like a thing balancing on its smaller end.

John Stuart Mill

What happens when each of these objects is slightly displaced?

The train *can* balance at the high point of a roller coaster but a slight disturbance
causes it to move rapidly away from its equilibrium position. The train is said to
be in *unstable equilibrium*. Compare this with the swing boat. When this is
disturbed, the resulting net forces will tend to restore it to its equilibrium
position. The swing is in *stable equilibrium*.

You would like a garage door to be in equilibrium in any position so that a
breath of wind does not bring it crashing on to your car. It is safest when the
forces acting are always balanced so that it is in *neutral equilibrium*.

Think of other objects which can be placed in positions of stable or unstable
equilibrium. What happens to the centre of mass when each is displaced by a
small amount?

When you balance a coin on its edge, its centre of mass is at its highest point and
displacing the coin lowers the centre of mass. The potential energy is at a
maximum in the upright position. Conversely, the potential energy of a swing is
at a minimum when it is hanging in equilibrium.

In this chapter energy principles are used to find positions of equilibrium and determine their nature and also to analyse the oscillations about positions of stable equilibrium which are caused by small displacements. It is assumed that all forces are conservative so that total energy is conserved. This means that forces such as friction are assumed to be negligible.

You might be surprised to learn that energy methods often provide an easier way to find equilibrium positions than analysing resultant forces and taking moments.

Potential energy at equilibrium

Consider a body modelled as a particle which is able to move in one dimension, such as a ball hanging on the end of an elastic string. Assume that its displacement from a fixed position is denoted by x and also that all forces acting are conservative, so that the energy equation applies.

$$\text{kinetic energy} + \text{potential energy} = \text{constant}$$
$$\tfrac{1}{2}mv^2 + V(x) = E$$

where the potential energy $V(x)$ is the total of *all* types of energy due to position x. In the case of the ball this is the total of gravitational and elastic energy. It is often denoted by $V(x)$ to indicate that it is simply a function of the position of the body but abbreviated to V in equations. Differentiating the energy equation with respect to x gives

$$mv\frac{\mathrm{d}v}{\mathrm{d}x} + \frac{\mathrm{d}V}{\mathrm{d}x} = 0.$$

Now $mv\dfrac{\mathrm{d}v}{\mathrm{d}x} = ma = F$, by Newton's second law where F is the resultant force acting on the particle. So

$$F + \frac{\mathrm{d}V}{\mathrm{d}x} = 0$$

$$\Rightarrow \qquad F = -\frac{\mathrm{d}V}{\mathrm{d}x}$$

But a particle is in equilibrium if and only if the resultant force is zero. Hence $\dfrac{\mathrm{d}V}{\mathrm{d}x} = 0$ in an equilibrium position.

The potential energy has a stationary value if and only if the body is in an equilibrium position.

Sometimes the position of a body is specified not by its displacement from a given position but by some other variable. For example, the position of a pendulum is usually expressed by giving the angle θ it makes with the vertical (see figure 5.1).

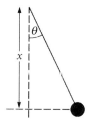

Figure 5.1

Then the derivative with respect to *this* variable is still zero at equilibrium, since by the chain rule

$$\frac{\mathrm{d}V}{\mathrm{d}\theta} = \frac{\mathrm{d}V}{\mathrm{d}x}\frac{\mathrm{d}x}{\mathrm{d}\theta} = 0 \quad \text{when} \frac{\mathrm{d}V}{\mathrm{d}x} = 0.$$

This argument can be applied not just to a particle but to a more general system, provided that it is constrained to move in such a way that its position, and therefore its potential energy, can be specified by the value of a single variable: normally an angle or a displacement. The conclusion is

> when a body acted on by conservative forces is free to move so that its potential energy can be given as a function V(x) of a single variable x, its equilibrium positions are given by the stationary values of V with respect to this variable.

EXAMPLE 5.1

One end of an elastic string of natural length *l* and modulus λ is fixed to the ceiling and a ball of mass *m* is attached to the other end so that the string hangs vertically. Show, *using energy methods*, that in equilibrium the string is stretched an amount $\dfrac{mgl}{\lambda}$.

SOLUTION

Figure 5.2

In figure 5.2, OA represents the position of the unstretched string. Consider the potential energy of the system when the mass is displaced *x* below A. The elastic energy is $\dfrac{\lambda x^2}{2l}$. The gravitational energy, relative to the level of point A, is $-mgx$: negative because the ball is below A. So the total potential energy is

$$V = \frac{\lambda x^2}{2l} - mgx$$

$$\Rightarrow \quad \frac{dV}{dx} = \frac{\lambda x}{l} - mg$$

When $\dfrac{dV}{dx} = 0$, $\quad \dfrac{\lambda x}{l} - mg = 0$

$$\Rightarrow \qquad\qquad x = \frac{mgl}{\lambda} \qquad\qquad\qquad ①$$

Note

The choice of the horizontal through A as the zero level of gravitational potential energy is arbitrary. Any fixed point will do. Changing V by a constant does not affect the result when $\dfrac{dV}{dx}$ is found.

This familiar example shows the energy method works, even though in this case simply balancing the forces $(mg = T = \dfrac{\lambda x}{l})$ gives equation ① immediately and is rather easier. The following examples show that energy methods can often be a quicker way of locating equilibrium positions than considering forces.

EXAMPLE 5.2

Figure 5.3 shows a uniform ladder AB of mass m and length $2l$ resting in equilibrium with its upper end A against a smooth vertical wall and its lower end B on a smooth inclined plane. The inclined plane makes an angle θ with the horizontal and the ladder makes an angle ϕ with the wall.

What is the relationship between θ and ϕ?

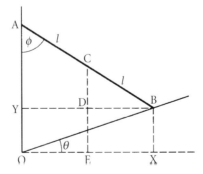

Figure 5.3

SOLUTION

There is no friction at A and B, so the reaction forces do no work when the ladder moves. The equilibrium position can thus be found using the energy method. The only contribution to the potential energy of the system is the gravitational force, which may be considered to act at the centre of the ladder, C.

Note that ϕ varies as the ladder moves, but θ, the inclination of the plane to the ground, is constant. The energy can be expressed in terms of a single variable, ϕ.

Take the ground level OX as the zero level of gravitational energy. The height of C above this level is

$$CE = CD + DE = CD + BX$$
$$= l\cos\phi + OX\tan\theta$$
$$= l\cos\phi + 2l\sin\phi\tan\theta$$

$(OX = YB = 2l\sin\phi)$

Hence the potential energy is

$$V = mg\,(l\cos\phi + 2l\sin\phi\tan\theta)$$
$$\frac{dV}{d\phi} = mgl(-\sin\phi + 2\cos\phi\tan\theta)$$

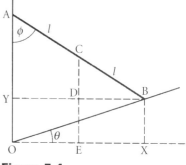

Figure 5.4

Equilibrium occurs when $\dfrac{dV}{d\phi} = 0$, that is when

$$-\sin\phi + 2\cos\phi\tan\theta = 0$$

Hence $\tan\phi = 2\tan\theta$ at equilibrium.

 Any fixed level can be taken as the reference for zero energy; OX is the most convenient here. It would be wrong to choose the zero energy level through A or B because A and B are not fixed.

The next example shows a situation with more than one equilibrium position.

EXAMPLE 5.3

A uniform rod OQ of mass m and length a is smoothly jointed to a fixed point at O, so that it can rotate in a vertical plane. P is a fixed point vertically above O so that $OP = a$. The ends of an elastic string of length a and modulus $2mg$ are connected to P and Q.

(i) Find the potential energy of the system when the rod makes an angle θ with the upward vertical, assuming the string is stretched.

Hence find positions of equilibrium of the rod.

(ii) Are there any other equilibrium positions when the string is unstretched?

(You may assume that the string is attached in such a way that the rod can rotate completely in the vertical plane without being caught up by the string.)

SOLUTION

(i) Figure 5.5 shows the position when the rod makes a general angle θ clockwise from the upward vertical with $0 \leqslant \theta \leqslant \pi$. The string is just taut when triangle OPQ is equilateral, that is $\theta = \dfrac{\pi}{3}$.

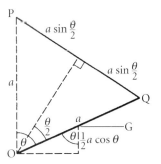

Figure 5.5

Consider the rod when in the general position *with the string taut*, that is $\theta > \dfrac{\pi}{3}$. Then

$$PQ = 2a \sin \frac{\theta}{2}$$

so the extension is $x = 2a \sin \dfrac{\theta}{2} - a$. The elastic energy is then

$$\frac{\lambda x^2}{2a} = \frac{2mg \left(2a \sin \dfrac{\theta}{2} - a \right)^2}{2a}$$

$$= mga \left(2 \sin \frac{\theta}{2} - 1 \right)^2$$

The centre of mass of the rod is at the mid-point G, so the gravitational potential energy, referred to zero level through O, is $mg \times$ height of G above O, that is $mg \left(\frac{1}{2} a \cos \theta \right)$. This remains correct when $\theta > \dfrac{\pi}{2}$, as $\cos \theta$ is then negative *and* G is *below* O.

The total potential energy is

$$V = mga \left(\frac{1}{2} \cos \theta \right) + mga \left(2 \sin \frac{\theta}{2} - 1 \right)^2$$

Differentiating to find the equilibrium points gives

$$\frac{\mathrm{d}V}{\mathrm{d}\theta} = -mga \left(\frac{1}{2} \sin \theta \right) + 2mga \left(2 \sin \frac{\theta}{2} - 1 \right) \cos \frac{\theta}{2}$$

$$= -mga \left(\sin \frac{\theta}{2} \cos \frac{\theta}{2} \right) + 2mga \left(2 \sin \frac{\theta}{2} - 1 \right) \cos \frac{\theta}{2}$$

$$= mga \cos\frac{\theta}{2}\left(-\sin\frac{\theta}{2} + 4\sin\frac{\theta}{2} - 2\right)$$

$$- mga \cos\frac{\theta}{2}\left(3\sin\frac{\theta}{2} - 2\right)$$

Equilibrium points are given when $\dfrac{dV}{d\theta} = 0$ that is when

$$\cos\frac{\theta}{2} = 0 \quad \text{or} \quad \sin\frac{\theta}{2} = \frac{2}{3}$$

$$\Rightarrow \quad \frac{\theta}{2} = \frac{\pi}{2} \quad \text{or} \quad \frac{\theta}{2} = \arcsin\frac{2}{3} = 0.730 \ \text{(3 significant figures)} \quad \text{or} \quad \pi - 0.730$$

$$\Rightarrow \quad \theta = \pi \quad \text{or} \quad \theta = 1.46 \quad \text{(or } 2\pi - 1.46 \text{ giving the position left of OP).}$$

The three equilibrium positions with the string taut, are shown in Figure 5.6.

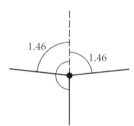

1.46   1.46

Figure 5.6

(ii) It remains to look at the case when the string is *unstretched*, $\theta < \dfrac{\pi}{3}$. In this case, the equilibrium position is the one where the rod is balanced vertically upwards. The energy method confirms this: only the gravitational term $mga\left(\frac{1}{2}\cos\theta\right)$ contributes to the potential energy and this has a stationary value at $\theta = 0$.

 Remember when using calculus that the angle θ must be in radians.

Consider a bead threaded on a smooth wire bent as shown in figure 5.7 and held in a vertical plane.

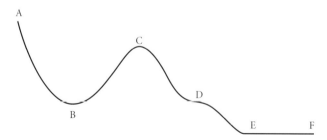

A

C

D

B

E   F

Figure 5.7

At which points on the curve can the bead be in equilibrium?

Think about what happens when the bead is slightly displaced from each of these points.

Which are positions of stable equilibrium?

In Example 5.3 there are three equilibrium positions: $\theta = 0$, π and 1.46 (ignoring the symmetrical case). But not all of these are stable.

Which do you think are stable and which unstable?

The potential energy can be written

$$V = mga\left[\tfrac{1}{2}\cos\theta + \left(2\sin\frac{\theta}{2} - 1\right)^2\right] \text{ when } \frac{\pi}{3} \leq \theta \leq \pi$$

$$V = mga\left(\tfrac{1}{2}\cos\theta\right) \qquad\qquad \text{ when } 0 < \theta \leq \frac{\pi}{3} \text{ (string not taut).}$$

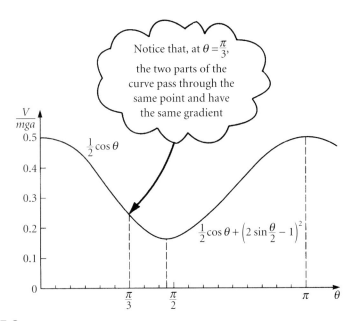

> Notice that, at $\theta = \frac{\pi}{3}$, the two parts of the curve pass through the same point and have the same gradient

Figure 5.8

The graph in figure 5.8 shows how the potential energy varies with θ.

Can you infer any relationship between the type of stationary point of a potential energy curve and the stability of the equilibrium position?

Condition for stability of equilibrium

Suppose the potential energy V has a *minimum*, V_0, at the equilibrium position x_0. Displacing the body from its equilibrium position is equivalent to supplying a small amount of kinetic energy K_0 in the form of a velocity taking it away from the equilibrium position. Assume this is in the direction of increasing x (see figure 5.9).

During the subsequent motion

$$V + K = \text{ constant } E = V_0 + K_0$$

where K denotes the kinetic energy.

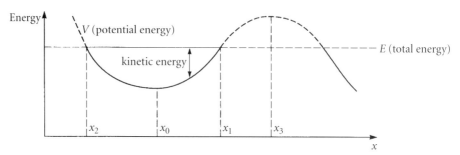

Figure 5.9

The graph shows the potential energy $V(x)$ and total energy E of the body at points near x_0. The difference $E - V(x)$ is the kinetic energy. You can see that at the point x_1, the kinetic energy is zero. It cannot become negative so the body cannot move past x_1 (dotted region of curve). Furthermore, since x_1 is *not* a position of equilibrium, the body begins to return to its equilibrium position. When it returns to x_0, it will have some velocity so will continue to a point x_2 and oscillate about the position of equilibrium. This is what is meant by a position of *stable equilibrium*: the body returns after a small displacement.

Note, if K_0 is greater leading to a *large* displacement past the point x_3, this would take the body into a new energy region and it would not return to x_0.

ACTIVITY 5.1

Show that when V is a maximum at the equilibrium position, and the body is given a small displacement, the kinetic energy *increases* and the body moves further from the equilibrium point. Draw an equivalent graph to that in figure 5.9 (remember that $E \geqslant V(x)$). Show that the equilibrium position is then unstable.

Summary of stability criteria

The results can be summarised as follows.

- The potential energy is a minimum $\Leftrightarrow$ a stable equilibrium point:
  $V'(x) = 0$, $V''(x) > 0$
- The potential energy is a maximum $\Leftrightarrow$ an unstable equilibrium point:
  $V'(x) = 0$, $V''(x) < 0$

? There are other types of equilibrium position. For example, imagine a ball on a horizontal surface. V = constant, $\dfrac{dV}{dx} = 0$ and a displacement does not result in any force. This is known as neutral equilibrium. Suppose the potential energy graph has a point of inflexion. What could this represent? Would you describe it as stable or unstable?

EXAMPLE 5.4

The potential energy of a particle is given by the equation $V = \dfrac{Ae^{kx}}{x}$.

Show that it has one position of equilibrium and that this is stable.

SOLUTION

$$\frac{dV}{dx} = \frac{A(xke^{kx} - e^{kx})}{x^2}$$

$$= \frac{Ae^{kx}}{x^2}(kx - 1)$$

$e^{kx} \neq 0$, so $\dfrac{dV}{dx} = 0$ when $kx - 1 = 0$, i.e. when $x = \dfrac{1}{k}$.

When x is just less than $\dfrac{1}{k}$, $\dfrac{dV}{dx} < 0$.

When x is just greater than $\dfrac{1}{k}$, $\dfrac{dV}{dx} > 0$.

> Sometimes this method of determining the nature of a stationary point is easier than differentiating twice.

So $x = \dfrac{1}{k}$ gives minimum potential energy and the equilibrium is stable.

EXAMPLE 5.5

A smooth circular hoop of radius a is fixed in a vertical plane. A small smooth ring of mass m is threaded on the hoop and is joined to the highest point of the hoop by a light elastic spring of natural length d and stiffness k, where $ka^2 - mga > 0$. At time t, the angle between the spring and the downward vertical is θ where $-\dfrac{\pi}{2} < \theta < \dfrac{\pi}{2}$.

(i) Show that the potential energy, V, relative to the highest point of the hoop, can be written in the form

$$V = 2(ka^2 - mga)\cos^2\theta - 2kad\cos\theta + \tfrac{1}{2}kd^2.$$

(ii) Given that $d < 2\left(a - \dfrac{mg}{k}\right)$, show that there are three positions of equilibrium. Discuss the stability of each position.

(iii) In the case when $d > 2\left(a - \dfrac{mg}{k}\right)$, show that there is just one equilibrium

position and that this position is stable.

(iv) Discuss briefly the case when $d = 2\left(a - \dfrac{mg}{k}\right)$.

[MEI]

SOLUTION

(i) When the spring has extension x

$$V = -mg(d + x)\cos\theta + \tfrac{1}{2}kx^2$$

$$= -mg \times 2a\cos\theta\cos\theta + \tfrac{1}{2}k(2a\cos\theta - d)^2$$

$$= 2(ka^2 - mga)\cos^2\theta - 2kad\cos\theta + \tfrac{1}{2}kd^2$$

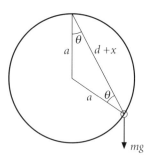

Figure 5.10

(ii) $V'(\theta) = -4(ka^2 - mga)\cos\theta\sin\theta + 2kad\sin\theta$

$$= 2a\sin\theta\big[kd - 2(ka - mg)\cos\theta\big]$$

$$= 4a(ka - mg)\sin\theta\left[\dfrac{kd}{2(ka - mg)} - \cos\theta\right] \qquad \text{①}$$

Let $\dfrac{kd}{2(ka - mg)} = c$ $\qquad$ $c > 0$ as $ka^2 > mga$

When $d < 2\left(a - \dfrac{mg}{k}\right)$, $c < 1$, so there are three solutions to $V'(\theta) = 0$ (when

$\sin\theta = 0$ or $\cos\theta = c$), giving three positions of equilibrium.

These are $\theta = 0$ and $\theta = \pm\alpha$, where $\cos\alpha = c$.

differentiate ①

$$V''(\theta) = 4a(ka - mg)\cos\theta(c - \cos\theta) + 4a(ka - mg)\sin^2\theta$$

maximum P.E.

$$\Rightarrow \qquad V''(0) = 4a(ka - mg)(c - 1) < 0 \qquad \text{so } \theta = 0 \text{ is unstable}$$

minimum P.E.

$$V''(\pm\alpha) = 4a(ka - mg)\sin^2\alpha > 0 \qquad \text{so } \theta = \pm\alpha \text{ are stable}$$

(iii) When $d > 2\left(a - \dfrac{mg}{k}\right)$, $c > 1$ so $\cos\theta = c$ is impossible.

There is just one position of equilibrium when $\theta = 0$.

$V''(0) = 4a(ka - mg)(c - 1) > 0$ so this position is stable.

(iv) When $d = 2\left(a - \dfrac{mg}{k}\right)$, $c = 1$ so $\alpha = 0$ and there is only one position of equilibrium.

Now $V''(0) = 0$, so investigate signs of $V'(\theta)$ near $\theta = 0$.

$$V'(\theta) = 4a(ka - mg)\sin\theta\,(1 - \cos\theta) \qquad \text{from } ①$$

$$= 4a(ka - mg)\sin\theta \times 2\sin^2\frac{\theta}{2}$$

This changes from negative to positive as θ increases from negative to positive so $\theta = 0$ gives a minimum for $V(\theta)$ and hence a position of stable equilibrium.

Note

Potential energy as a function of several variables

The discussion of stationary values of potential energy *V* has been confined to the case when *V* can be expressed as a function of a *single* variable, such as distance or angle. In this case, the system is said to have 'one degree of freedom'. In fact, the principle that equilibrium positions coincide with stationary values of potential energy extends to systems with more than one degree of freedom, i.e. where *V* is a function of *several* variables. Handling stationary values of functions of several variables is beyond the scope of this course. However, the following investigation demonstrates the energy principle in use in such a case. Although the problem has two degrees of freedom (the potential energy can be expressed as a function of two variables), this complication does not have to be considered in the investigation.

Using potential energy to find the shortest path connecting points

Mechanics can be used to solve *geometrical* problems. You are given three points, representing villages perhaps, and you want to find the shortest length of path which connects all three to a single point, such as a well.

Figure 5.11

As you will see, this can be solved by thinking about an experiment in mechanics. It is even more interesting to *do* the experiment, if you have the equipment.

The theoretical model

Imagine a smooth horizontal plane lamina with three holes in it at positions A, B, C, representing the positions of three villages. Three strings are threaded as shown (they need not be of equal length), tied together at P and pass smoothly through the holes. At the end of each is a weight W. The system is allowed to rest in equilibrium.

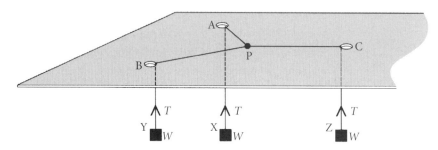

Figure 5.12

(i) Write down the potential energy of the system in terms of string lengths, and deduce that the total length PA + PB + PC must have a minimum value in the equilibrium position.

(ii) Show that when the triangle ABC has no angle greater than 120°, P takes up a position where ∠BPA = ∠APC = ∠CPA = 120°. This configuration represents the solution to the problem.

(iii) Show that when ∠BAC (say) in the triangle ABC is greater than 120°, you could not have an equilibrium position with P inside the triangle. What would then happen if you performed the experiment? What is the solution to the problem in this case?

(iv) Does the experiment extend to four or more points?

The actual experiment

The experiment works very well if you use small pulleys at A, B and C and adjust their angles to the final directions of the strings. Try it with various positions of A, B and C, including a case where $\angle BAC > 120°$.

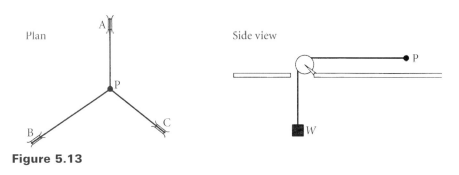

Figure 5.13

❷ Small oscillations about stable equilibrium

When a system is displaced from a position of stable equilibrium it usually oscillates about this position. You have already met systems like this such as the spring–mass oscillator and simple pendulum in which small oscillations have been modelled by simple harmonic motion. It is possible to use the energy equation to obtain an approximation to simple harmonic motion in the more complex systems you have met in this chapter.

In general the energy equation is:

$$\tfrac{1}{2}m\dot{x}^2 + V(x) = \text{constant}.$$

Differentiating this with respect to t gives:

$$m\dot{x}\,\ddot{x} + V'(x)\dot{x} = 0$$

$$\Rightarrow \qquad\qquad \ddot{x} = -\frac{1}{m}V'(x) \qquad\qquad ①$$

When $V'(x)$ is a linear function of x, this gives the simple harmonic motion equation directly, but see the comment on page 159.

The potential energy of a ball of mass m hanging on the end of an elastic string of stiffness k and with extension x, for example, can be written as

$$V(x) = \tfrac{1}{2}kx^2 - mgx$$

$$\Rightarrow \qquad V'(x) = kx - mg.$$

Substituting in ① gives

$$\ddot{x} = -\frac{1}{m}(kx - mg).$$

The equilibrium position is when $x = \dfrac{mg}{k} = x_0$ so

$$\ddot{x} = -\dfrac{k}{m}(x - x_0)$$

which is simple harmonic motion about $x = x_0$.

Writing $y = x - x_0$ gives the standard equation

$$\ddot{y} = -\omega^2 y$$

with $\omega^2 = \dfrac{k}{m}$.

When the potential energy is a function of an angle, θ, the kinetic energy can usually be written in the form $K\dot{\theta}^2$ and you can differentiate the energy equation with respect to t to give a similar result with x replaced by θ.

It is often the case, however, that $V'(x)$ or $V'(\theta)$ is not a linear function of x or θ and then you need to find a linear approximation for it. You have met an example of this in the case of the simple pendulum where $\sin\theta$ is written as θ when θ is small. You can often find an approximation using series expansions or trigonometrical methods, but the following method, using the second derivative of the potential energy at the equilibrium position, is often simpler.

Figure 5.14 shows the graph of $V'(x)$.

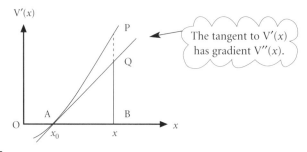

Figure 5.14

The gradient of $V'(x)$ at x_0 is

$$V''(x_0) = \dfrac{QB}{AB} = \dfrac{QB}{x - x_0}.$$

When $(x - x_0)$ is small, $QB \approx PB = V'(x)$.

$$\Rightarrow \quad V''(x_0) \approx \dfrac{V'(x)}{x - x_0}$$

$$\Rightarrow \quad V'(x) \approx (x - x_0)V''(x_0).$$

> This is the linear approximation for $V'(x)$ in terms of x.

The simple harmonic motion approximation for small oscillations about the equilibrium position x_0 can then be found using equation ①.

$$m\ddot{x} = -V'(x)$$

so $\quad m\ddot{x} = -(x-x_0)V''(x_0)$

$\Rightarrow \quad \ddot{x} = -\dfrac{V''(x_0)}{m}(x-x_0).$

Replacing $(x-x_0)$ by y gives

$$\ddot{y} = -\omega^2 y$$

with $\quad \omega^2 = \dfrac{V''(x_0)}{m}.$

Notice that this motion is simple harmonic motion only if $V''(x_0)$ is positive, which is the condition for stable equilibrium.

EXAMPLE 5.6

Figure 5.15 shows a spring controlled flap. The flap can be modelled as a uniform rectangular lamina of length AB = $2l$, smoothly hinged about an axis through B. The spring BD is horizontal and is connected by a cord passing over a smooth pulley C and attached to the flap at A. BC = $2l$. When the flap is horizontal (A is at C), the spring has its natural length l. The modulus λ of the spring is $\frac{1}{4}mg$.

(i) Write down the potential energy of the system when the flap makes an angle θ with the horizontal.

Hence show that $\theta = \dfrac{\pi}{4}$ is an equilibrium position.

(ii) Differentiate the energy equation to give the equation of motion and express this in terms of $\phi = \theta - \dfrac{\pi}{4}$.

Hence show that the period of small oscillations about the equilibrium

position is $\dfrac{2\pi}{\omega}$, where $\omega^2 = \dfrac{3\sqrt{2g}}{4l}$

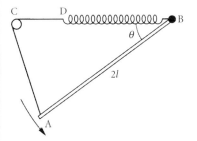
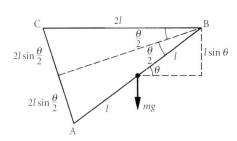

Figure 5.15

SOLUTION

(i) When the flap makes an angle θ with the horizontal, the spring is extended

from its natural length by $CA = 4l\sin\left(\dfrac{\theta}{2}\right).$

Elastic P.E. $= \dfrac{\lambda}{2l}\left(4l\sin\dfrac{\theta}{2}\right)^2 = 2mgl\sin^2\dfrac{\theta}{2}$ (since $\lambda = \tfrac{1}{4}mg$).

Gravitational P.E. $= -mgl\sin\theta$ when BC is the zero level.

Total P.E. $= V = 2mgl\sin^2\dfrac{\theta}{2} - mgl\sin\theta$.

Differentiate to find the equilibrium position

$$\dfrac{dV}{d\theta} = 2mgl\sin\dfrac{\theta}{2}\cos\dfrac{\theta}{2} - mgl\cos\theta$$

$$= mgl\sin\theta - mgl\cos\theta \qquad \text{①}$$

When $\dfrac{dV}{d\theta} = 0, \quad \sin\theta = \cos\theta$

$\Rightarrow \qquad \theta = \dfrac{\pi}{4}$.

$\dfrac{d}{d\theta}\left(\sin^2\dfrac{\theta}{2}\right) = \left(2\sin\dfrac{\theta}{2}\cos\dfrac{\theta}{2}\right)\times\dfrac{1}{2}$

$= \sin\dfrac{\theta}{2}\cos\dfrac{\theta}{2}$

(ii) When the flap is moving, P.E. + K.E. is constant.

The moment of inertia of the flap, rotating about a pivot through one end is $\tfrac{4}{3}ml^2$. So the kinetic energy of the flap is

$$\tfrac{1}{2}\left(\tfrac{4}{3}ml^2\right)\dot\theta^2 = \tfrac{2}{3}ml^2\dot\theta^2$$

Therefore

$$\tfrac{2}{3}ml^2\dot\theta^2 + V = \text{constant}$$

Differentiate with respect to t to give the equation of motion

$$\tfrac{2}{3}ml^2\times 2\dot\theta\ddot\theta + \dfrac{dV}{d\theta}\dot\theta = 0$$

$$\Rightarrow \qquad \left(\dfrac{4ml^2}{3}\right)\ddot\theta = -V'(\theta) \qquad \text{②}$$

$$= -mgl(\sin\theta - \cos\theta) \qquad \text{from ①}$$

$$V''(\theta) = +mgl(\cos\theta - \sin\theta)$$

$$\Rightarrow \qquad V''\left(\dfrac{\pi}{4}\right) = \sqrt{2}mgl$$

Using the linear approximation $V'(\theta) = \left(\theta - \dfrac{\pi}{4}\right)V''\left(\dfrac{\pi}{4}\right)$ in equation ② gives

$$\left(\dfrac{4ml^2}{3}\right)\ddot\theta \approx -\left(\theta - \dfrac{\pi}{4}\right)\times\sqrt{2}mgl$$

$$\Rightarrow \qquad \ddot\theta = \dfrac{-3\sqrt{2}}{4l}g\left(\theta - \dfrac{\pi}{4}\right)$$

which is simple harmonic motion about $\theta = \dfrac{\pi}{4}$ with period $\dfrac{2\pi}{\omega}$ where $\omega^2 = \dfrac{3\sqrt{2}}{4l}g.$

Note

You can also use trigonometry to solve this problem, by replacing θ with $\dfrac{\pi}{4} + \phi$ and writing $\sin \phi \approx \phi$.

EXERCISE 5A

Some parts of the questions in this exercise relate to enrichment material. They are marked with the **e** *icon.*

1 (i) Explain what is meant by a system being
   (a) in equilibrium
   (b) in stable equilibrium.
   (ii) Give an example of a system in which a particle is in
   (a) stable equilibrium
   (b) unstable equilibrium.

A smooth wire is fixed in a vertical plane and is defined by

$$y = \frac{1}{10a^4}\left(\tfrac{1}{5}x^5 + \tfrac{1}{4}ax^4 - 4a^2x^3\right) \qquad -5a \leqslant x \leqslant 4.7a$$

where y is measured vertically upwards and x is a horizontal co-ordinate. The form of the wire is shown in the diagram.

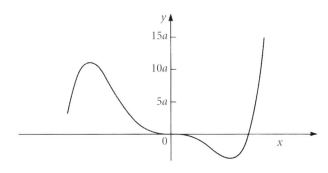

   (iii) Copy the diagram and, given that there is a small bead threaded on the wire, mark on your diagram the equilibrium positions of the bead, noting whether each position is stable (S) or unstable (US). Also calculate the exact locations of the equilibrium positions.
   (iv) Describe the motion (no calculations are necessary) when the bead is released, in turn from
   (a) the point $(-4.5a, 9.8a)$
   (b) the point $(2a, -2.16a)$
   (c) the point on the wire where $y = 15a$.

[Oxford]

2 A particle P of mass m moves along the line of greatest slope of a smooth plane which makes an angle θ with the horizontal. The particle is attached to one end of a light elastic string, the other end of which is fixed to a point O on the plane. The natural length of the string is a and its modulus is $2mg$.

   (i) Write down the gravitational potential energy of the particle when it is at a distance x down the plane from O. Take O as the zero energy level.

   (ii) Write down the elastic energy, assuming $x \geqslant a$ (i.e. the string is not loose).

   (iii) Denoting the total potential energy by V(x), find $\dfrac{dV}{dx}$ and hence find e, the value of x when the particle is in equilibrium.

   (e) (iv) Write down an energy equation (*kinetic + potential = E*, a constant) and differentiate with respect to t to give the equation of motion. Show that this can be written in the form $\ddot{x} = -\dfrac{2g}{a}(x - e)$.

   Hence deduce the period of oscillations about the equilibrium position, assuming the string remains taut.

3 A spring of modulus λ and natural length a is attached to a point P on the ceiling and an identical spring is attached to a point Q on the floor a distance $2a$ vertically below P. The other end of each spring is attached to a ball of mass m, so that it is free to oscillate in a vertical line.

   (i) Write down the gravitational potential energy and the elastic energy when the ball is displaced x below O, the mid-point of PQ. Hence deduce there is an equilibrium position at $x = \dfrac{mga}{2\lambda}$.

   (e) (ii) Differentiate the energy equation to show the equation of motion is

   $$\ddot{x} = -\frac{2\lambda}{ma}\left(x - \frac{mga}{2\lambda}\right).$$

   Hence write down the period of the oscillation about the equilibrium position.

4 In the diagram, ABC represents a light spring of natural length $2a$ and modulus of elasticity λ, which is coiled round a smooth horizontal rod. B is the mid-point of AC. The two ends of a light inelastic string of length $2a$ are attached to the spring at A and C. A particle of mass m is fixed to the string at its mid-point D. Thus, as the particle descends vertically, the spring is compressed.

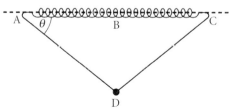

(i) Obtain an expression for the total potential energy of the system in terms of θ, the angle DAB.

(ii) Hence show that, if $\theta = \dfrac{\pi}{6}$ is an equilibrium position, $mg = \lambda\left(\dfrac{2}{\sqrt 3} - 1\right)$.

[O & C, *adapted*]

5 A uniform rod OA of length $2a$ and mass m is freely pivoted to a fixed point at O. The end A is attached by a light elastic string of natural length a and modulus λ to a point B a distance $2a$ vertically above O. When the rod is in a general position, the angle AOB is denoted by 2θ.

(i) Find the gravitational potential energy with respect to O, and the elastic energy, as functions of θ.

(ii) Show there is always one position of equilibrium with the string stretched and determine the condition of λ for there to be a second.

(iii) Discuss the nature of the stability in each case.

6 A small lamp of mass m is at the end A of a light rod AB of length $2a$ attached at B to a vertical wall in such way that the rod can rotate freely about B in a vertical plane perpendicular to the wall. A spring CD of natural length a and modulus of elasticity λ is joined to the rod at its mid-point C and to the wall at a point D a distance a vertically above B.

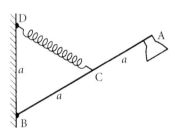

Show that if $\lambda > 4\,mg$ the lamp can hang in equilibrium away from the wall and find the angle DBA.

[O & C]

7 The diagram shows a smooth wire bent into the form of a circle in a vertical plane. A ring P is threaded on the circle and tied to a light inextensible string which passes over a pulley O at the highest point of the circle. A particle of the same mass as the ring hangs at the other end of the string. Use the energy method to find two positions of equilibrium, one stable and one unstable.

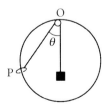

8 A smooth thin wire in the form of a semicircle of diameter d is fastened in a vertical plane with its ends A and B at the same horizontal level and uppermost. A smooth ring P of mass m is threaded on the wire and small smooth rings are fixed at A and B, An endless elastic band of natural length d and stiffness $\dfrac{kmg}{d}$ passes through the three rings but is otherwise unrestricted.

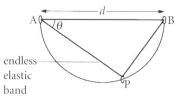

(i)   Write down the total gravitational and elastic energy of the system in terms of θ = angle PAB.

(ii) Show that there is a value of k for which P can be in equilibrium at every point of the wire between A and B.

(iii) Find the range of values of k for which there is just one stable equilibrium point.

9 In a diatomic molecule, one atom is very much heavier than the other and the lighter atom is free to move on a straight line through the centre of the heavier atom. The potential energy for the force between two atoms in a diatomic molecule can be represented approximately by

$$V(x) = -ax^{-6} + bx^{-12}$$

where x is the atomic separation and a and b are positive constants.

(i)   Locate any positions of stable equilibrium of the lighter atom.

(ii) Find the period of small oscillations about such positions, assuming the mass of the lighter atom is m.

(iii) Sketch the potential energy as a function of x. How does the force vary as the atoms approach each other?

[MEI, *adapted*]

10 Three points are defined by the vertices of an equilateral triangle which has medians of length $\dfrac{3a}{2}$ and lies in a vertical plane. One vertex is above the other two which lie at the same horizontal level. Three light springs of natural lengths a each have one end attached to a different vertex. Their free ends are joined together and lie at the intersection of the medians. A particle of mass m is fixed to this junction which falls under the influence of gravity. The configuration is shown in the diagram.

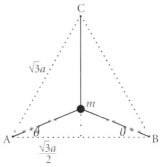

The spring attached to the top vertex has a stiffness $\dfrac{2mg}{a}$ and those attached

to the lower vertices have five times this stiffness.

(i) Show that the potential energy, V, of the system is given by

$$V = \tfrac{1}{4}mga(33\sec^2\theta - 40\sqrt{3}\sec\theta + 38)$$

where θ is the angle that one of the lower springs makes with the horizontal and the gravitational potential energy is taken relative to the horizontal line AB.

(ii) Show that one point of equilibrium occurs at $\theta = 0$ and locate any other equilibrium points.

(iii) By considering the behaviour of $\dfrac{dV}{d\theta}$ for small values of θ determine the

stability of equilibrium at $\theta = 0$.

[MEI]

11 A uniform circular cylinder of mass M and radius a lies at rest inside a fixed hollow cylinder of radius $3a$. The axes of both cylinders are horizontal. A particle of mass m is fixed to a point at the top of the inner cylinder which can roll without slipping inside the hollow cylinder. The system is subject to a vertical gravitational field g.

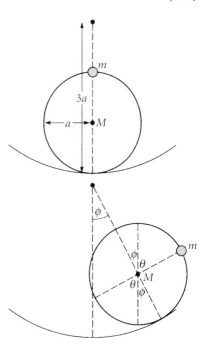

(i) Show that $\phi = \tfrac{1}{2}\theta$, where ϕ and θ are as shown in the diagram.

(ii) Find an expression for the gravitational potential energy of the system as a function of θ.

(iii) Locate the positions of equilibrium and determine the relationship between M and m for the initial position to be one of stable equilibrium. Show that in this case it is the only equilibrium position.

[MEI]

12 A light plane uniform square lamina of side $2a$ is mounted in a vertical plane and is free to rotate about an axis through its centre and perpendicular to its plane. Initially two of the edges of the lamina are horizontal. A particle of mass km, $k > 0$, is attached to the centre of the upper edge and particles of mass m are attached to each of the two bottom corners.

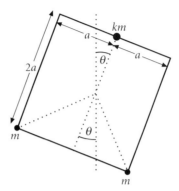

(i) By considering a rotation through an angle θ of the lamina show that the potential energy of the system relative to the centre of the lamina is $mga(k - 2) \cos \theta$.

(ii) Locate any positions of equilibrium.

(iii) Discuss the dependence of the nature of the stability of any equilibrium positions on the value of k.

e **(iv)** Given that $k = 1$ and the mass of the lamina can be neglected write down the energy equation. By differentiating this equation with respect to time find the period of small oscillations of the lamina about the position of stable equilibrium.

[**MEI**]

13 A particle is subject to an attractive force of magnitude kx^2 towards a fixed point, where k is a constant and x is the distance of the particle from the fixed point.

(i) Show that the potential energy of the particle relative to the fixed point is $\frac{1}{3}kx^3$.

A particle lies on the line segment joining two fixed points, A and B, which are a distance d apart. The particle is subject to forces of attraction towards each of the points, the magnitude of each force being proportional to the square of the distance of the particle from the point. The constants of proportionality are a^2 and b^2 respectively.

(ii) Write down an expression for the potential energy of the particle as a function of its distance x from the point A.

(iii) Show that there is a single point of equilibrium, determine its position, and show that the equilibrium is stable.

e **(iv)** Given that the mass of the particle is m, find the period of small oscillations about this point of stable equilibrium in terms of a, b, d and m.

[**MEI**]

14 (i) State the condition to be satisfied by the potential energy V of a particle at a point of stable equilibrium.

A particle of mass m moves along the positive x axis under the influence of a force. The potential energy at a point with co-ordinate x is

$$V(x) = k\frac{e^{ax}}{x},$$

where k and a are positive constants.

(ii) Find the position of equilibrium of the particle and show that it is stable.

e **(iii)** Find the approximate periodic time of small oscillations of the particle about this position of stable equilibrium.

[MEI]

15 Four light rods each of length $2a$ are freely hinged at their ends to form a rhombus ABCD which is suspended at A from a fixed point. A light spring of natural length $2a$ and stiffness $\dfrac{3mg}{a}$ connects the points A and C. A particle of mass $\dfrac{3m}{2}$ is attached at the point C and each of the rods AB and AD carries a particle of mass m at its mid-point. The arrangement is shown in the diagram.

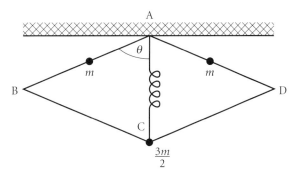

(i) Show that the potential energy V of the system relative to the zero level through A is given by

$$V = mga(24\cos^2\theta - 32\cos\theta + 6).$$

(ii) Deduce that there are two positions of equilibrium and show that only one of these is stable.

The system now performs small oscillations about the position of stable equilibrium where $\theta = \alpha$.

(iii) Show that the kinetic energy T is given by

$$T = ma^2\dot{\theta}^2(13 - 12\cos^2\theta).$$

(iv) By putting $\theta = \alpha + \phi$ and assuming that both ϕ and $\dot{\phi}$ remain very small, show that

$$T \approx \frac{23}{3} ma^2 \dot{\phi}^2.$$

(e) You are now given that, near the equilibrium position,

$$V \approx \frac{mga}{3}(-14 + 40\phi^2).$$

(v) Find the approximate period of small oscillations about the position of stable equilibrium.

[MEI]

KEY POINTS

1 When a body acted on by *conservative* forces is free to move so that its potential energy can be given as a function $V(x)$ of a single variable x, its equilibrium positions are given by the stationary values of $V(x)$ with respect to this variable.

2 A *minimum* value of potential energy corresponds to a position of *stable* equilibrium; a *maximum* value to a position of *unstable* equilibrium.

(e) Small oscillations about positions of stable equilibrium can generally be modelled by simple harmonic motion. The equation of motion can be derived by differentiating the energy equation with respect to time.

(e) The linear approximation

$$V'(x) = (x - x_0)V''(x_0)$$

can be used when $x \approx x_0$. It might be convenient to transform the variable representing displacement so that it has a zero level at the equilibrium position.

Appendix 1: Calculus methods

Differentiation

Product rule $\qquad y = uv, \dfrac{dy}{dx} = v\dfrac{du}{dx} + u\dfrac{dv}{dx}$

Quotient rule $\qquad y = \dfrac{u}{v}, \dfrac{dy}{dx} = \dfrac{v\dfrac{du}{dx} - u\dfrac{dv}{dx}}{v^2}$

Chain rule $\qquad y = f(u), u = g(x) \qquad \dfrac{dy}{dx} = \dfrac{dy}{du} \times \dfrac{du}{dx}$

Kinematics $\qquad v = \dfrac{ds}{dt}$

$$a = \dfrac{dv}{dt} = \dfrac{d^2 s}{d^2 t} = v\dfrac{dv}{ds}$$

Standard derivatives

$f(x)$	$f'(x)$	$f(x)$	$f'(x)$
x^n	nx^{n-1}	e^{kx}	ke^{kx}
$\ln x$	$\dfrac{1}{x}$	$\ln [g(x)]$	$\dfrac{g'(x)}{g(x)}$
$\sin kx$	$k\cos kx$	$\cos kx$	$-k\sin kx$
$\tan kx$	$k\sec^2 kx$	$\sec x$	$\sec x \tan x$
$\cot x$	$-\csc^2 x$	$\csc x$	$-\csc x \cot x$
$\arcsin x$	$\dfrac{1}{\sqrt{1-x^2}}$	$\arccos x$	$-\dfrac{1}{\sqrt{1-x^2}}$
$\arctan x$	$\dfrac{1}{1+x^2}$		

Integration

By substitution
$$\int f'(u)\frac{du}{dx}dx = f(u) + c$$

By parts
$$\int u\frac{dv}{dx}dx = uv - \int v\frac{du}{dx}dx$$

Volume of revolution

About the x axis $\int_a^b \pi y^2 \, dx$

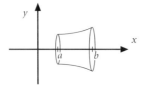

About the y axis $\int_p^q \pi x^2 \, dy$

Standard integrals

$f(x)$	$\int f(x)\,dx$ (+ a constant)	$f(x)$	$\int f(x)\,dx$ (+ a constant)
x^n	$\dfrac{x^{n+1}}{n+1}, \quad n \neq -1$	e^{kx}	$\frac{1}{k}e^{kx}$
$\dfrac{1}{x}$	$\ln|x|, \quad x \neq 0$	$\dfrac{g'(x)}{g(x)}$	$\ln|g(x)|$
$\sin kx$	$-\frac{1}{k}\cos kx$	$\cos kx$	$\frac{1}{k}\sin kx$
$\sec^2 kx$	$\frac{1}{k}\tan kx$	$\tan x$	$\ln|\sec x|$
$\cot x$	$\ln|\sin x|$	$\dfrac{1}{x^2 - a^2}$	$\dfrac{1}{2a}\ln\left|\dfrac{x-a}{x+a}\right|$
$\dfrac{1}{\sqrt{a^2 - x^2}}$	$\arcsin\left(\dfrac{x}{a}\right), \quad |x| < a$	$\dfrac{1}{a^2 + x^2}$	$\dfrac{1}{a}\arctan\left(\dfrac{x}{a}\right)$
$\dfrac{1}{a^2 - x^2}$	$\dfrac{1}{2a}\ln\left|\dfrac{a+x}{a-x}\right| = \dfrac{1}{a}\operatorname{arctanh}\left(\dfrac{x}{a}\right), \quad |x| < a$		

Appendix 2: Solving differential equations

The general solution of a second-order linear equation

For $\dfrac{d^2y}{dx^2} + a\dfrac{dy}{dx} + by = f(x)$

the *auxiliary equation* is $\lambda^2 + a\lambda + b = 0$ with roots λ_1, λ_2.

The *complementary function* (C.F.) satisfies the equation with $f(x)$ replaced by zero, that is

$y = Ae^{\lambda_1 x} + Be^{\lambda_2 x}$	if λ_1, λ_2 are real and $\lambda_1 \neq \lambda_2$
$y = Ae^{\lambda x} + Bxe^{\lambda x}$	if λ_1, λ_2 are real and $\lambda_1 = \lambda_2 = \lambda$
$y = e^{\alpha x}(A\sin\beta x + B\cos\beta x)$	if $\lambda_1 = \alpha + \beta j$ and $\lambda_2 = \alpha - \beta j$

The *particular integral* (P.I.) is any function which satisfies the full equation.

The *general solution* is $y = $ C.F. + P.I.

Example 1

It is useful to know more than one way of solving problems. The solution of the second-order equation from Example 1.8 on page 34 is summarised here.

Newton's second law of motion of a raindrop gives $mg - kv = m\dfrac{d^2s}{dt^2}$.

Writing v as $\dfrac{ds}{dt}$ and rearranging gives $\dfrac{d^2s}{dt^2} + \dfrac{k}{m}\dfrac{ds}{dt} = g$.

This is in the standard form for a second-order linear differential equation with no term in s.

The *auxiliary equation* is

$$\lambda^2 + \left(\frac{k}{m}\right)\lambda = 0 \qquad \text{giving } \lambda = 0 \text{ or } \frac{-k}{m}.$$

So the *complementary function* is

$$s = A\,e^{0t} + B\,e^{-kt/m} = A + B\,e^{-kt/m}.$$

The *particular integral* is $s = \dfrac{mgt}{k}$, so that the general solution of the equation is

$$s = A + B\,e^{-kt/m} + \frac{mgt}{k} \qquad\qquad \left(V_T = \frac{mg}{k} \right)$$

or $\qquad s = A + B\,e^{-gt/V_T} + V_T t.$

Since $s = 0$ when $t = 0$, $A + B = 0$, so $A = -B$.

Also $v = \dfrac{ds}{dt} = -\left(\dfrac{Bg}{V_T}\right)e^{-gt/V_T} + V_T$

Now $v = 0$ when $t = 0$, so $\dfrac{Bg}{V_T} - V_1 \rightarrow B = \dfrac{V_T^2}{g} = A$.

This gives the solution, as before $s = V_T t - \dfrac{V_T^2}{g}(1 - e^{-gt/V_T})$.

Note that this method would not work with a kv^2 law of resistance as the resulting second-order equation would be non-linear and the standard methods of solution would not apply.

Example 2: Simple harmonic motion

Another example is the simple harmonic equation $\dfrac{d^2 x}{dt^2} + \omega^2 x = 0$.

Here the *particular integral* is $x = 0$ and the *auxiliary equation* is $\lambda^2 + \omega^2 = 0$ giving $\lambda = 0 \pm i\omega$.

The *complementary function* is then $x = A \sin \omega t + B \cos \omega t = a \sin(\omega t + \varepsilon)$ where

$a = \sqrt{A^2 + B^2}$ and $\sin \varepsilon = \dfrac{B}{a}$ and $\cos \varepsilon = \dfrac{A}{a}$.

The equations $v^2 = \omega^2(a^2 - x^2)$ and $T = \dfrac{2\pi}{\omega}$ follow from this, as described in *Mechanics 3*.

The integrating factor method for a first-order equation

This is another possible method of solving some of the equations in this book.

For $\dfrac{dy}{dx} + Py = Q$, where P, Q are functions of x only:

The *integrating factor* is $R = e^{\int P dx}$.

The solution is $Ry = \int RQ dx$.

For more details of both methods you should consult *Differential Equations*.

Answers

Chapter 1

❓ (Page 1)

The forces are air resistance and the gravitational forces due to the Earth and the moon. This is discussed more fully in the section on gravitational force, see page 12.

Activity 1.1 (Page 4)

$\arccos\left(\dfrac{x}{a}\right)$

❓ (Page 8)

Because the acceleration is not constant.

Exercise 1A (Page 10)

1 (i) $\arcsin\left(\dfrac{v}{2}\right)$

   (ii) $\dfrac{\pi}{6}$

   (iii) $6\arcsin\left(\dfrac{2y}{3}\right)$

2 (i) $\dfrac{1}{2}\arctan\left(\dfrac{x}{2}\right)$

   (ii) $\dfrac{\pi}{8}$

3 In the following answers, k is an arbitrary constant.

   (i) $s=\dfrac{1}{2}v+k$

   (ii) $v=ke^{2t}$

   (iii) $v=-\dfrac{2}{3}\cos 3t + k$

   (iv) $v=\dfrac{1}{t+k}$

   (v) $v=ke^{-s}$

   (vi) $v=\sqrt{4s(1-s)+k}$

   (vii) $s=-\dfrac{1}{3}\ln k(3v+2)$

   (viii) $s=\dfrac{1}{2}\ln(1+v^2)+k$

4 (i) $\dfrac{16}{3}$

   (ii) $\dfrac{1}{2}$

   (iii) $\sqrt{2\ln 2}$ or 1.177

   (iv) $7\dfrac{1}{2}$

   (v) $\dfrac{\pi}{4}$ or 0.785

   (vi) $\dfrac{1}{3}\ln\dfrac{5}{2}$ or 0.305

   (vii) $\dfrac{1}{2}\ln 3$ or 0.549

   (viii) $\dfrac{1}{2}\ln\dfrac{4}{3}$ or 0.144

5 (i) $v\dfrac{dv}{ds}=\dfrac{1}{v+2}$

   (iii) $\dfrac{dv}{dt}\approx\dfrac{1}{v+2}$

   (v) $s=-2t+\dfrac{1}{3}(4+2t)^{3/2}-\dfrac{8}{3}$

Activity 1.2 (Page 14)

(i) $u=\sqrt{\dfrac{2g}{R_{\mathrm{E}}}R_{\mathrm{P}}}$

(ii) $11.2\ \mathrm{ms}^{-1}$

(iii) You probably could hit a tennis ball into space from the surface of an asteroid. You probably could not jump off into space.

❓ (Page 15)

The period is approximately 0.25% less at the poles.

Exercise 1B (Page 16)

1 (i) $\mathrm{M}^{-1}\mathrm{L}^3\mathrm{T}^{-2}$

   (ii) $a_h=\dfrac{GM}{(R+h)^2}, a_0=g$

   (v)   1.6%

2 (ii) $\dfrac{R^2 g}{r^2}$

3 (i) $\sqrt{\dfrac{k}{R}}$

   (ii) $k=4.9\times 10^{12}$, $1673\ \mathrm{ms}^{-1}$

4 (i) $\left(\dfrac{r}{R}\right)^3 M$

(ii) $\dfrac{GMr}{R^3}$

(iii) Period $2\pi\sqrt{\dfrac{R^3}{GM}}$

5 (i) $\dfrac{GM_m}{(d-x)^2} - \dfrac{GM_e}{x^2}$

(iii) $v - \sqrt{2\left(\dfrac{GM_m}{d-x} + \dfrac{GM_e}{x} - \dfrac{GM_m}{d-R} - \dfrac{GM_e}{R}\right) + u^2}$

(iv) $v^2 > 0$ when $x = d\left[1 + \sqrt{\dfrac{M_m}{M_e}}\right]^{-1}$

Activity 1.3 (Page 22)

$E = \frac{1}{2}mv^2 + \frac{1}{2}kx^2 - mg(x+l)$

Acceleration $= g - \dfrac{k}{m}x$ which is simple harmonic

motion about $x = \dfrac{mg}{k}$.

Exercise 1C (Page 27)

1 $\frac{1}{6}J$

2 (i) 75 J

(ii) $\sqrt{15}$ or 3.87 ms^{-1}

(iii) $10\sqrt{15}$ or 38.7 Ns

(iv) $10\sqrt{15}$ or 38.7 Ns

3 (i) $\sqrt{\dfrac{40}{3}}$ or 3.65 ms^{-1}

(ii) $10\sqrt{\dfrac{40}{3}}$ or 36.5 Ns

4 (i) $\dfrac{dv}{dt} = \dfrac{10}{v}$

(ii) $v = \sqrt{20t + 25}$

(iv) $s = \frac{1}{30}(v^3 - 125)$

(v) Start from $v\dfrac{dv}{ds} = \dfrac{10}{v}$

5 (i) $\frac{1}{2}mga$

(ii) $\sqrt{ga}$

6 (i) $\frac{1}{2}mu^2 - mgR$

(ii) 11.3 kms^{-1}

7 (ii) $\frac{1}{3}\sqrt{\dfrac{2}{G}}(h^{3/2} - R^{3/2})$

8 (ii) At 40 ms^{-1} the acceleration is zero.

(iii) $t = 16\ln\left(\dfrac{1600}{1600 - v^2}\right)$, 23.2 seconds

9 (i) $\dfrac{7g}{80}$ or 0.858 ms^{-2}

(ii) 313 m

11 (i) $p + \dfrac{q}{v}$

(ii) $p + \dfrac{q}{v} = m\dfrac{dv}{dt}$

12 (i) $MF(1 - e^{-at}) - Mbv = M\dfrac{dv}{dt}$

(iii) $x = \dfrac{F}{b}\left\{t - \dfrac{a+b}{ab} + \dfrac{1}{ab(a-b)}(b^2e^{-at} - a^2e^{-bt})\right\}$

13 (i) $-\dfrac{mgR^2}{(R+x)^2} = ma$

(ii) $H = \dfrac{RU^2}{2gR - U^2}$

(iii) $P = -\dfrac{mgR^2}{R+x}$

(iv) (a) $x \to H$, max $P = -\dfrac{mgR^2}{R+H}$

(b) $H \to \infty$, $x \to \infty$, the particle escapes. $P \to 0$ as $x \to \infty$.

❓ (Page 33)

The gradient of the graph at the origin is g. Use the trapezium rule to find the area under graph up to $t \approx 5$ when v is 31.5.

Activity 1.4 (page 34)

(i)

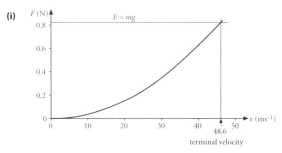

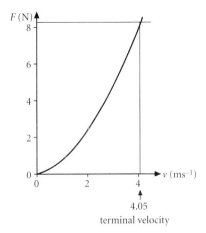

F (N)
8
6
4
2
0
0   2   4   → v (ms^{-1})

4.05
terminal velocity

(ii) The v term makes a difference in the second case (the terminal velocity is $4.86\,\text{ms}^{-1}$ if it is ignored), but not much.

(iii) The v^2 term is the most important for the puffball.

❷ (Page 39)

Yes, if it is given a large initial velocity, for example a gunshot. It will then slow down to its terminal velocity.

A ball takes longer to come down.

Exercise 1D (Page 39)

1 (i) $\dfrac{g}{100} - kv^2 = \dfrac{1}{100}\dfrac{\mathrm{d}v}{\mathrm{d}t}$, $v_\text{T} = \dfrac{1}{10}\sqrt{\dfrac{g}{k}}$

(ii) $k = \dfrac{g}{22\,500} = 4.36 \times 10^{-4}$

(iii) $\dfrac{15}{\sqrt{2}}$ or $10.61\,\text{ms}^{-1}$

2 (i) $m = 3.4 \times 10^{-15}$ (kg)

(ii) $m\dfrac{\mathrm{d}v}{\mathrm{d}t} = mg - 3.1\times10^{-10}v$, $v_\text{T} = 1.1 \times 10^{-4}\,\text{ms}^{-1}$

(iii) 1.5 micron

3 $0.74\,\text{ms}^{-1}$

4 (i) $40\dfrac{\mathrm{d}v}{\mathrm{d}t} = -kv$

(ii) $ue^{-k/40}$

(iv) 18.6 m

5 (i) Weight $\frac{4}{3}\pi R^3 \rho_\text{w} g$,

$2R^2(\rho_\text{g} - \rho_\text{w})g - 9\eta v = 2R^2\rho_\text{g}\dfrac{\mathrm{d}v}{\mathrm{d}t}$

(iii) Terminal velocity of 1 cm marble $\frac{1}{9}\,\text{ms}^{-1}$, of 2 cm marble $\frac{4}{9}\,\text{ms}^{-1}$

(iv) $\frac{1}{60}\ln 100 = 0.077$ seconds

6 (i) $k = \dfrac{mg}{40}$

(ii) $F = mg\sin 2° + \dfrac{mgv}{40}$

(iii) $m\dfrac{\mathrm{d}v}{\mathrm{d}t} = -\left(mg\sin 2° + \dfrac{mgv}{40}\right)$

(iv) 66 m

7 (i) $\dfrac{\mathrm{d}v}{\mathrm{d}x} = g\left(\dfrac{1}{v} - \dfrac{1}{V}\right)$

8 (iii) $\dfrac{UV}{\sqrt{U^2 + V^2}}$

(iv) $v = V\tan\left(\alpha - \dfrac{gt}{V}\right)$ where $\alpha = \arctan\left(\dfrac{U}{V}\right)$

10 (i) $v\dfrac{\mathrm{d}v}{\mathrm{d}x} = av - bv^2$

(ii) $\dfrac{a}{b}$ is the terminal velocity. $\dfrac{a}{b} + B$ is the initial velocity.

(iii) $B = V + \dfrac{a}{b}$

11 (i) $mv\dfrac{\mathrm{d}v}{\mathrm{d}x} = \dfrac{P}{v} - mkv^2$

(ii) The acceleration is zero when $v = A$, so A is the terminal velocity; $\dfrac{1}{3k}\ln\left(\dfrac{A^3}{A^3 - V_0^3}\right)$

(iv) (a) The area under the graph of $\dfrac{v^4}{A^3 - v^3}$ increases more rapidly as v increases.

(b) If m is reduced, A increases and W decreases.

12 (i) 1250 N

(ii) $62.5\,\text{ms}^{-1}$

(iii) 0.531 m

(iv) 78.1 J

13 (i) $mk(A^2 - v^2) - Bmv^2 = ma$

(iv) $x = \dfrac{1}{c}\ln\left(\dfrac{e^{V_0ct} + e^{-V_0ct}}{2}\right)$

Chapter 2

❷ (Page 46)

1 See text that follows the question.

2 Less because it loses the momentum given to the coal.

Exercise 2A (Page 54)

1 (i) $\dfrac{d(mv)}{dt} = 0$

(ii) $\dfrac{d(mv)}{dt} = -mg$

(iii) $m\dfrac{dv}{dt} = F$

2 (ii) $v = \dfrac{F}{Mk}(e^{kt} - 1)$

3 $\dfrac{F}{k}\ln\left(\dfrac{M}{M - m_0}\right)$

4 (ii) $v^2 = \dfrac{2000P}{r}\ln\left(\dfrac{M_0}{M_0 - rt}\right)$

5 (ii) $F = (M - ks)v\dfrac{dv}{ds}$

6 (iii) $\dfrac{P}{v} = M\left(1 - \dfrac{t}{2T}\right)^3\dfrac{dv}{dt}$

7 (i) $k = \dfrac{1}{T}\ln 2$

(ii) $Mge^{kt} = \dfrac{d}{dt}(Me^{kt}v)$

(iv) $\dfrac{gT^2}{2(\ln 2)^2}(2\ln 2 - 1)$

9 (i) Dimensions of k are MT^{-1}

(iv) $v = \dfrac{g}{3km^2}(m^3 - M^3)$

11 (iii) $v = \dfrac{\rho g(r^4 - a^4)}{4kr^3}$

(iv) $\dfrac{dv}{dt} = g - \dfrac{3g}{4r^4}(r^4 - a^4)$

12 (ii) $v^2 = \dfrac{2g}{3k(1+kx)^2}\left[(1+kx)^3 - 1\right](\sin\alpha - \mu\cos\alpha)$

(iii) Acceleration approaches $\dfrac{g}{3}(\sin\alpha - \mu\cos\alpha)$, a constant

13 (ii) $\dfrac{c}{k}\left[(1 + k^2t^2)^{\frac{1}{2}} - 1\right]$

14 (i) (a) $\dfrac{dm}{dt} = mkv$

(b) $\dfrac{d(mv)}{dt} = -mg$

(ii) $v = \sqrt{\dfrac{g}{k}(1 - e^{-2kx})}$

Investigations (Page 67)

Multistage rockets

(i) $u\ln\left(\dfrac{1}{1 - \alpha + \dfrac{\alpha}{N}}\right)$

(ii) $u\ln\left(\dfrac{1}{1 - \alpha}\right)$

(iii)

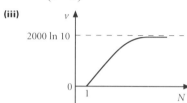

Two-stage rockets

For example, taking N as 9, the maximum velocity gain is when r is $\dfrac{1}{3}$.

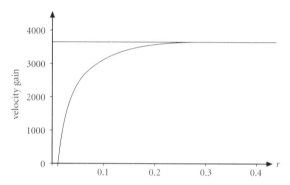

The relationship between r and N when the gain is a maximum is $r^2N = 1$; the relationship between v_1 and v_2 is $v_1 = v_2$.

Exercise 2B (Page 69)

1 $m\dfrac{dv}{dt} = kc$; the balloon loses elastic energy.

2 (ii) In order, the expulsion speeds in ms^{-1} are: 617, 602, 598, 803, 803, 798, 806; there are probably two different fuels.

3 (ii) 1290 ms^{-1}

5 (i) $m\dfrac{dv}{dt} = ku$

7 (i) $M_0 - kt$, $\dfrac{\alpha M_0}{k}$

(iv) $R_1 = \dfrac{M_0}{M_0 - \alpha M_1}$, $R_2 = \dfrac{1}{1 - \alpha}$

(v) $c\ln R_1$

(vi) $c\ln R_1 R_2$

8 Speed $c \ln\left(\dfrac{1}{1-\alpha}\right) - \dfrac{g\alpha M}{k}$; altitude

$\dfrac{Mc}{k}[(1-\alpha)\ln(1-\alpha)+\alpha] - \dfrac{1}{2}g\dfrac{\alpha^2 M^2}{k^2}$

9 (i) $m = M_0 - kt$

 (ii) Because $\dfrac{dv}{dt}$ must be positive

 (iv) $c\ln\left(\dfrac{M_0 g}{kc}\right) - \left(\dfrac{M_0 g}{k} + c\right)$

10 (i) $m = M - kt, \dfrac{\alpha M}{k}$

 (iii) $c\ln\left(\dfrac{1}{1-\alpha}\right)$

Chapter 3

❓ (Page 74)

The outside child has the greater energy. For the other answers, see the text that follows the question.

❓ (Page 79)

Position A gives the greatest radius of gyration because much of the mass is further from the axis. Position B gives the least radius of gyration because this position is the nearest to the centre of mass (see the parallel axes theorem, pages 94 to 96).

Exercise 3A (Page 80)

1 (i) $2ma^2, \frac{2}{3}Ma^2; 5ma^2, \frac{5}{3}Ma^2$

 (ii) $2ma^2, \frac{1}{2}Ma^2; ma^2, \frac{1}{4}Ma^2; 4Ma^2, Ma^2$

 (iii) $\frac{1}{2}ma^2, \frac{1}{6}Ma^2; \frac{3}{4}ma^2, \frac{1}{4}Ma^2; 2ma^2, \frac{2}{3}Ma^2; ma^2,$

 $\frac{1}{3}Ma^2$

 (iv) $2ma^2, \frac{2}{5}Ma^2; \frac{11}{4}ma^2, \frac{11}{20}Ma^2$

2 (i) 0.3125 kg m^2

 (ii) 1172 J

3 11.85 J

4 (i) 25 J

 (ii) 70.7 rad s^{-1}

Exercise 3B (Page 89)

1 (i) $\rho\delta x$

 (ii) $x^2\rho\delta x$

 (iii) $\displaystyle\int_0^{2a} x^2 \rho \, dx = \frac{8}{3}\rho a^3$

 (iv) $M = 2a\rho$

 (v) $\frac{4}{3}Ma^2$

2 (i) 7.47 kg m^2

 (ii) 23.3 J

3 (i) $\pi\rho y^2 \delta x$

 (iii) $\frac{8}{15}\rho\pi r^5$

 (iv) $M = \frac{4}{3}\pi r^3 \rho$

 (v) $\displaystyle\int \frac{1}{2}\rho\pi y^4 dx$

4 (i) $I = 9.83 \times 10^{37}$ kg m^2 ; K.E. $= 2.6 \times 10^{29}$ J, overestimate

 (ii) 2.9×10^{23} J

 (iii) 3.75×10^{28} J

 (iv) approx $7:1$

5 (i) $\dfrac{M}{\pi r^2 h}$

 (ii) $4.41h$

 (iii) $0.824Mr^2$

 (iv) $1.65:1$

6 (i) $2\pi\sigma r^2 \cos\theta\delta\theta$

 (ii) $\frac{2}{3}Mr^2$

Exercise 3C (Page 98)

1 (i) **(a)** $6ma^2$ **(b)** $3ma^2$ **(c)** $3ma^2$

 (iii) **(a)** $13ma^2$ **(b)** $\frac{33}{4}ma^2$

2 (ii) $\frac{1}{3}n(4n+1)Ma^2$

3 See table on pages 179–180

4 (i) $\frac{1}{2}Mr^2$

 (ii) **(a)** $\frac{1}{4}Mr^2; \frac{1}{6}Mr^2; \frac{1}{8}Mr^2; \frac{1}{10}Mr^2; \frac{1}{12}Mr^2$

 (b) $\frac{1}{2}mr^2; \frac{1}{2}mr^2; \frac{1}{2}mr^2; \frac{1}{2}mr^2; \frac{1}{2}mr^2$

 (iii) $\frac{1}{4}Mr^2$. The first is $\frac{1}{4}Mr^2 = \frac{1}{4}mr^2$ and the third is

 $\frac{1}{16}Mr^2 = \frac{1}{4}mr^2$. In the other three diagrams some of the sectors are not distributed about the axis in the same way as the shaded sector.

5 (i) $\sqrt{x_p^2 + y_p^2}$

 (ii) $\sum m_p(y_p^2 + z_p^2), \sum m_p(x_p^2 + z_p^2)$

 (iii) $I = I_x = I_y = I_z$ by symmetry

6 (i) $\rho\delta x$

 (ii) $\rho\delta x(x \sin\alpha)^2$

(iii) $\frac{2}{3}\rho a^3 \sin^2 \alpha$

(iv) $\frac{1}{3}Ma^2 \sin^2 \alpha$

(v) $\frac{1}{3}Ma^2 \sin^2 \alpha$

(vi) The moment of inertia will be multiplied by $\sin^2 \alpha$.

7 (i) $2y\sigma\delta x$

(ii) $\frac{2}{3}\sigma y^3 \delta x$

(iii) $y = \frac{ax}{h}, \ \frac{2\sigma a^3}{3h^3}\int_0^h x^3 dx$

(iv) $\frac{1}{6}Ma^2$

(v) Because the moment of inertia about the y axis is $\delta m x^2$.

(vi) $\frac{1}{2}Mh^2$

(vii) $\frac{1}{6}M(a^2 + 3h^2)$

(viii) $\frac{1}{18}M(3a^2 + h^2)$

9 (i) $\pi y^2 \rho \delta x$

(iii) $\int_0^h \frac{1}{2}\pi\rho y^4 \, dx$

(iv) $y = \frac{rx}{h}, \ \frac{1}{10}\pi\rho r^4 h$

(v) $M = \frac{1}{3}\pi r^2 h\rho, \ \frac{3}{10}Mr^2$

10 (i) $2\pi ab^2, \ 2\pi ab^2 \rho$

(ii) $\frac{4}{3}Mab$

11 (i) $\frac{2}{5}Mb^2$

(ii) $\frac{2}{5}Ma^2$

(iii) These are equal to the moments of inertia of spheres of radius b and a about their diameters.

12 $\frac{3}{20}M(r^2 + 4h^2)$

13 (i) For the z axis, $r^2 = x^2 + y^2$ so $I_x = \Sigma my^2$

(iii) (a) $\frac{1}{3}M(a^2 + b^2 + 3ac + 3c^2)$

(b) $\frac{1}{3}M(b^2 \cos^2 \theta + a^2 + 3ac + 3c^2)$

14 (i) $\frac{4}{3}\pi a^2 \rho, \frac{4}{3}\pi b^2 \rho, \frac{8}{15}\pi a^5 \rho, \frac{8}{15}\pi b^5 \rho$

(iii) 8.816×10^{37} kg m^2

16 (i) $I_x = I_y = \frac{1}{4}M_1 b^2$

Exercise 3D (Page 112)

1 Rod **(i)** a^2 **(ii)** $\frac{2}{3}a$ **(iii)** $\frac{1}{2}a^4 = \frac{1}{2}Ma^2$

Disc **(i)** $\frac{2}{3}\pi ka^3$ **(ii)** At O **(iii)** $\frac{2}{5}\pi ka^5 = \frac{3}{5}Ma^2$

Rod **(i)** $\frac{a(2p+aq)}{2}$ **(ii)** $\frac{a(3p+2aq)}{3(2p+aq)}$

(iii) $\frac{a^3(4p+3aq)}{12} = \frac{Ma^2}{6}\frac{(4p+3aq)}{(2p+aq)}$

Pipe **(i)** $3\pi rkh^2$ **(ii)** $\frac{5}{9}h$ **(iii)** $3\pi r^3 kh^2 = Mr^2$

2 (i) $3\rho - \frac{2\rho y}{h}$

(ii) $2\pi a^2 \rho h$

(iii) $\frac{5}{12}h$

(iv) $\pi a^4 \rho h = \frac{1}{2}Ma^2$

3 (iv) C, $\sqrt{35ga}$

4 (ii) (a) $\frac{1.04g}{l}$

(b) $\sqrt{4.16gl}$

5 (i) $143ma^2$

(ii) $\sqrt{\frac{124g}{143a}}$

6 (i) $\frac{1}{2}ma^2$

(ii) 19.9 cm

7 (i)

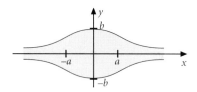

(ii) $M = 2\pi\rho a^2 b$

(iii) $I = Ma^2$

8 (ii) $\frac{3}{10}Ma^2$

(iii) $\frac{1}{2}ma^2, \ m = \frac{4}{5}M$

Answers to Exercise 3C, Question 3

Uniform body of mass M	Axis	Moment of inertia
Hoop of radius r	Through centre $\perp$ to plane	Mr^2
Hollow cylinder radius r	Through centre $\perp$ to circular cross-section	Mr^2
Thin ring radius r	Diameter	$\frac{1}{2}Mr^2$
Thin ring radius r	Through edge $\perp$ to plane	$2Mr^2$
Thin ring radius r	Tangent	$\frac{3}{2}Mr^2$
Disc of radius r	Through centre $\perp$ to plane	$\frac{1}{2}Mr^2$
Solid cylinder radius r	Through centre $\perp$ to circular cross-section	$\frac{1}{2}Mr^2$

Uniform body of mass M	Axis	Moment of inertia
Thin disc radius r	Diameter	$\frac{1}{4}Mr^2$
Thin disc radius r	Through edge $\perp$ to disc	$\frac{3}{2}Mr^2$
Thin disc radius r	Tangent	$\frac{5}{4}Mr^2$
Thin rod	Parallel to rod at distance d	Md^2
Thin rod of length $2l$	Through centre $\perp$ to rod	$\frac{1}{3}Ml^2$
Thin rod of length $2l$	Through end $\perp$ to rod	$\frac{4}{3}Ml^2$
Rectangular lamina	In plane, through centre $\perp$ to sides length $2l$	$\frac{1}{3}Ml^2$
Rectangular lamina	Edge $\perp$ to sides length $2l$	$\frac{4}{3}Ml^2$

Uniform body of mass M	Axis	Moment of inertia
Rectangular lamina sides $2a$ and $2b$	Through centre $\perp$ to plane	$\frac{1}{3}M(a^2+b^2)$
Rectangular block sides $2a$, $2b$ and $2c$	Through centre parallel to sides of length $2c$	$\frac{1}{3}M(a^2+b^2)$
Solid sphere radius r	Diameter	$\frac{2}{5}Mr^2$
Solid sphere radius r	Tangent	$\frac{7}{5}Mr^2$
Hollow sphere radius r	Diameter	$\frac{2}{3}Mr^2$
Hollow sphere radius r	Tangent	$\frac{5}{3}Mr^2$

Chapter 4

❓ (Page 116)

When the angular momentum of the ice-skater is conserved, a reduction in the moment of inertia leads to an increase in angular speed (see page 135).

Investigation (Page 125)

Assuming no rope is left on the drum, the speed is approximately 6.6 ms⁻¹.

Exercise 4A (Page 127)

1 (i)   0.0241 kg m²
   (ii)   105 rad s⁻²
   (iii)   2.53 Nm
   (iv)   1.19 kJ

2 (i)   5.4 kg m²
   (ii)   10.5 J
   (iii)   1.97 rad s⁻¹

3 (i) 4.608×10^{-3} Nm
   (ii)   (a) 1.91×10^{-3} J (b) 0.869 J (c) 234 000 J
   (iii) $1 : 454 : 1.22 \times 10^8$

4 (i)   250 rad s⁻²
   (ii)   0.8 rad
   (iii)   150 N
   (iv)   167 N
   (v)   2.4 rad

5 (i)   0.0573 J
   (iii)   0.209 rad s⁻², 0.098 kg m²
   (iv)   0.18 kg m²
   Much of the mass is near the centre of the wheel so reducing the moment of inertia.

6 (i)   0.054 kg m²
   (iii)   0.9 seconds

7 (i) $2000v$ rad s⁻¹
   (ii)   0.603 ms⁻¹

8 (ii) $\frac{1}{8}Mg$

Investigation (Page 133)

(i)   1m

(ii) $\frac{2}{3}$ m, $d = 1 \pm \sqrt{1 - 2r^2}$ so $r < 0.71$

(iii) $d < 0.75$ and the length of the rod is $< \sqrt{3}$.

There are two possible points of suspension if $1.5 < \text{length} < \sqrt{3}$.

Exercise 4B (Page 138)

1 (i) $\ddot{\theta} = -\left(\dfrac{3g}{4a}\right)\sin\theta$

   (ii) $2\pi\sqrt{\dfrac{4a}{3g}}$

   (iii) $\dfrac{4a}{3}$

2 (i) $\left(\dfrac{61}{3}\right)ml^2$

(ii) $I\ddot{\theta} = (mgl + 2mg \times 3l)\sin\theta,\ 2\pi\sqrt{\dfrac{61l}{21g}}$

(iii) 0.342 m

4 (i) $\dfrac{\omega}{2}$

(ii) $\dfrac{1}{4}a\omega^2 - g(1 - \cos\theta)$

(iii) $-\dfrac{1}{2}g\sin\theta$

5 (ii) $\dfrac{9J}{7ml}$

(iii) $2m\dfrac{\sqrt{7gl}}{3\sqrt{3}}$

6 (i) No centripetal force

(ii) $\dfrac{3}{2}Ma^2\omega$

(iii) No moment about the axis

7 (i) $\dfrac{pqa\omega}{p+q}$

(ii) $\dfrac{p\omega}{p+q},\ \dfrac{ap\omega}{b(p+q)}$

(iii) Reactions at the pivot produce an impulsive couple.

(iv) $\dfrac{pqa^2\omega^2}{2(p+q)}$

8 $\sqrt{7}a$

9 (iii) 228 (3 s.f.)

11 (ii) $\dfrac{5}{3}Ml^2$

(iii) (b) $2\pi\sqrt{\dfrac{5kl}{2\sqrt{3}g}}$

12 (ii) $4\pi a\sqrt{\dfrac{37}{k}}$

13 (iv) $\dfrac{15}{8}mg\cos\theta$

(v) $16°$

14 (i) $\dfrac{3}{13}(a + 4x)$

(ii) $6m\,(3a^2 + 2x^2)$

15 (i) $\dfrac{8}{3}ma^2$

(ii) $\dfrac{3\sqrt{2}J}{8ma}$

(iii) $\dfrac{8}{3}m\sqrt{\sqrt{2}ga}$

Chapter 5

❓ (Page 150)

There are points of equilibrium at B, C, D, and along EF.

For points between E and F the bead will stay put and is then said to be in *neutral* equilibrium. B is the only position of stable equilibrium.

❓ (Page 151)

Unstable for $\theta = 0$ and π, stable for $\theta = 1.46$.

There is a relationship between the type of stationary point of a potential energy curve and the stability of the equilibrium position; as discussed in the text that follows, a minimum implies a stable equilibrium point and a maximum implies an unstable equilibrium point.

Activity 5.1 (Page 152)

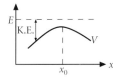

❓ (Page 153)

A stationary point of inflection is unstable. 'Upwards' displacement results in kinetic energy at the equilibrium position and so motion further away.

Investigation (Page 156)

(i) Denote PX by l_1, etc.
Total PE $= -W(l_1 + l_2 + l_3) + W(\text{PA} + \text{PB} + \text{PC})$

(ii) The triangle of forces is equilateral.

(iii) P would be pulled through the hole at A.
The shortest path is BA + AC.

(iv) Specifying that the paths converge gives both diagonals for a convex quadrilateral.

Exercise 5A (Page 161)

1 (i) (a) There is no resultant force.

(b) The system returns to the equilibrium position when displaced by a small amount.

(ii) **(a)** For example, a particle hanging on the end of a string.

(b) For example, a particle placed on top of a smooth sphere.

(iii) $(0, 0)$ is unstable, $(-4a, 11.5a)$ is unstable and $(3a, -3.9a)$ is stable.

(iv) **(a)** Falls off

(b) Oscillates about the lowest point

(c) Slides all the way along and falls off

2 **(i)** $-mgx \sin \theta$

(ii) $mg\dfrac{(x-a)^2}{a}$

(iii) $\dfrac{dV}{dx} = -mg \sin \theta + 2mg\dfrac{(x-a)}{a}$, $a(1 + \frac{1}{2}\sin \theta)$

(iv) Period $\pi\sqrt{\dfrac{2a}{g}}$

3 **(i)** $-mgx, \dfrac{\lambda x^2}{a}$

(ii) $2\pi\sqrt{\dfrac{ma}{2\lambda}}$

4 **(i)** $\lambda a(1 - \cos \theta)^2 - mga \sin \theta$

5 **(i)** $mga \cos 2\theta, \frac{1}{2}\lambda a(4 \sin \theta - 1)^2$

(ii) $\theta = \dfrac{\pi}{2}$ (unstable when $\lambda \geqslant \dfrac{mg}{3}$),

$\theta = \arcsin\left(\dfrac{\lambda}{4\lambda - mg}\right)$ provided $\lambda > \dfrac{mg}{3}$ (stable)

6 Angle DBA $= 2 \arcsin\left[\dfrac{\lambda}{2(\lambda - 2mg)}\right]$

7 $\theta = 0$ (stable) and $\theta = \dfrac{\pi}{3}$ (unstable)

8 **(i)** $\frac{1}{2}mgd[k + (k - 1) \sin 2\theta]$

(ii) $k = 1$

(iii) $k < 1$

9 **(i)** $x = \pm\left(\dfrac{2b}{a}\right)^{1/6}$

(ii) $\dfrac{\pi}{3}m^{1/2}(2b)^{2/3}a^{-7/6}$

(iii)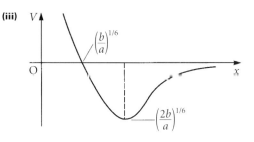

The force is repulsive when the atoms are closer than $\left(\dfrac{2b}{a}\right)^{1/6}$; otherwise it is attractive.

10 **(ii)** $\theta = \arccos\left(\dfrac{11\sqrt{3}}{20}\right) = 0.31$

(iii) Unstable

11 **(ii)** $-2(M + m)ga \cos \frac{1}{2}\theta + mga \cos \theta$ (relative to the centre of the larger cylinder)

(iii) Equilibrium when $\theta = 0$ or $\cos \frac{1}{2}\theta = \frac{1}{2}[1 + \dfrac{M}{m}]$; the initial position is stable when $M > m$.

12 **(ii)** $\theta = 0$ or π

(iii) When $k = 2$ both equilibrium positions are neutral.

When $k > 2$, $\theta = 0$ is unstable and $\theta = \pi$ is stable.

When $k < 2$, $\theta = 0$ is stable and $\theta = \pi$ is unstable.

(iv) $2\pi\sqrt{\dfrac{5a}{g}}$

13 **(ii)** $\dfrac{a^2x^3}{3} + \dfrac{b(d - x)^3}{3}$

(iii) $\dfrac{bd}{a + b}$

(iv) $2\pi\sqrt{\dfrac{m}{2abd}}$

14 **(i)** V must be a minimum.

(ii) $x = \dfrac{1}{a}$

(iii) $2\pi\sqrt{\dfrac{m}{ka^3 e}}$

15 **(ii)** $\theta = 0, \cos \theta = \frac{2}{3}$ (stable)

(v) $\pi\sqrt{\dfrac{23a}{10g}}$

Index